# Report Sheets

### to accompany

# Laboratory Experiments

### for

# World of Chemistry

Steven S. Zumdahl
Susan L. Zumdahl
Donald J. DeCoste

**McDougal Littell**
*A Houghton Mifflin Company*

Evanston, IL
Boston · New York

ISBN-13: 978-0-618-82971-2          ISBN-10: 0-618-82971-7

456789-VHO-11 10 09 08

# CONTENTS

To the Student.................................................................................................................vii

Safety in the Chemistry Laboratory .............................................................................. viii

First Aid in the Laboratory .............................................................................................. viii

Laboratory Safety Agreement ........................................................................................ix

Chapter 1:   **Chemistry: An Introduction**

   **1.** Chemistry of Fire..............................................................................1

   **2.** Scientific Observations.....................................................................5

   **3.** Observations and Explanations ........................................................9

Chapter 2:   **Matter**

   **4.** Physical and Chemical Changes.....................................................13

   **5.** Household Chemistry .....................................................................17

   **6.** Properties of Matter........................................................................21

   **7.** Separation Challenge......................................................................23

   **8.** The Sludge Test..............................................................................25

   **9.** Separation of Mixtures ...................................................................29

   **10.** Distillation....................................................................................35

Chapter 3:   **Chemical Foundations: Elements, Atoms, and Ions**

   **11.** Aluminum Atoms ..........................................................................39

   **12.** Electrolysis ...................................................................................43

   **13.** Classifying Elements ....................................................................45

   **14.** Electric Solutions .........................................................................49

Chapter 4:   **Nomenclature**

   **15.** Forming and Naming Ionic Compounds.......................................51

   **16.** Grocery Store Nomenclature.........................................................53

   **17.** Energy Changes in Physical and Chemical Systems......................55

Chapter 5:   **Measurements and Calculations**

   **18.** Measurement and the SI System ...................................................57

   **19.** Measuring a Book? Precisely!.......................................................61

   **20.** Conversion Factors........................................................................63

   **21.** Measurement and Density .............................................................69

Chapter 6:   **Chemical Composition**

   **22.** The Bean Lab ................................................................................73

   **23.** Decomposing Copper Oxide .........................................................77

   **24.** Formula for a Hydrate....................................................................79

**Chapter 7:**    **Chemical Reactions: An Introduction**

    **25.** Recognizing Chemical Reactions........................................83

    **26.** Examples of Chemical Reactions........................................87

    **27.** Interpreting Chemical Reactions.......................................89

    **28.** Conservation of Mass......................................................93

**Chapter 8:**    **Reactions in Aqueous Solutions**

    **29.** Reactions in Solution I: Precipitation.............................95

    **30.** Activity Series for Metals................................................99

    **31.** Unknown Solutions.......................................................101

    **32.** Qualitative Analysis: Anions.........................................105

    **33.** The Halide Family.........................................................109

**Chapter 9:**    **Chemical Quantities**

    **34.** Copper Wire in a Solution of Silver Nitrate...................113

    **35.** Mass Relationships in Chemical Compounds.................117

    **36.** The Calcium Content of Milk .......................................123

    **37.** Stoichiometry ...............................................................127

    **38.** Calorimetry and Limiting Reactants .............................131

    **39.** Synthesis of Manganese (II) Chloride...........................135

**Chapter 10:**   **Energy**

    **40.** Energy Value of Nuts....................................................139

    **41.** Specific Heat of Metal...................................................143

    **42.** Which is Your Metal?....................................................147

    **43.** Stoichiometry and Calorimetry ....................................151

    **44.** Heat of Reaction............................................................155

    **45.** Heats of Reaction and Hess's Law.................................159

**Chapter 11:**   **Modern Atomic Theory**

    **46.** Sunprint Paper Photography..........................................163

    **47.** Flame Tests...................................................................167

    **48.** Electron Probability.......................................................169

**Chapter 12:**   **Chemical Bonding**

    **49.** Dyes and Dyeing...........................................................173

    **50.** Models of Molecules.....................................................177

**Chapter 13:**   **Gases**

    **51.** Gas Laws and Drinking Straws......................................181

    **52.** Determining Absolute Zero............................................185

    **53.** The *P-n* Relationship of Gases.....................................187

    **54.** Molar Volume and the Universal Gas Constant..............191

**Chapter 14:** **Liquids and Solids**

**55.** Magic Sand.........................................................................................195

**56.** Freezing Point – A Physical Property ...............................................199

**57.** Heating and Cooling Behavior of a Pure Substance .........................203

**58.** Heat of Fusion of Ice........................................................................207

**59.** Energy and Changes of State.............................................................209

**60.** Vapor Pressure of Water – An Experimental Determination.............211

**Chapter 15:** **Solutions**

**61.** Solution Properties ............................................................................215

**62.** Polar and Nonpolar Solvents.............................................................219

**63.** Temperature and Solubility...............................................................223

**64.** Chloride in Water ..............................................................................227

**65.** Hard Water Analysis .........................................................................231

**Chapter 16:** **Acids and Bases**

**66.** Acids and Bases.................................................................................235

**67.** Acid Rain...........................................................................................241

**68.** Indicators...........................................................................................245

**69.** Analysis of Vinegar...........................................................................247

**70.** Quantitative Titration ........................................................................253

**71.** Conductivity Titrations – A CBL Investigation................................257

**72.** Acids, Bases, and Buffers..................................................................261

**Chapter 17:** **Equilibrium**

**73.** Iodine Clock Reaction .......................................................................265

**74.** Equilibrium Beads.............................................................................271

**75.** Equilibrium and Le Chatelier's Principle..........................................275

**76.** Chemical Equilibrium .......................................................................279

**77.** MOM and Your CBL .........................................................................283

**Chapter 18:** **Oxidation-Reduction Reactions and Electrochemistry**

**78.** Oxidation and Reduction....................................................................287

**79.** Activity Series ...................................................................................293

**80.** Halogen Activity Series.....................................................................297

**81.** Analysis of Hydrogen Peroxide ........................................................301

**82.** Galvanic Cells ...................................................................................305

**83.** Corrosion of Iron...............................................................................307

**Chapter 19:** **Radioactivity and Nuclear Energy**

**84.** Investigating Radioactivity................................................................311

**85.** The Half-Life of Pennies...................................................................315

Chapter 20: **Organic Chemistry**

    **86.** The Synthesis of Esters ...................................................................319

    **87.** Saponification....................................................................................323

    **88.** Synthesis of Slime ...........................................................................327

    **89.** Gluep ................................................................................................331

Chapter 21: **Biochemistry**

    **90.** Enzymes in Food .............................................................................333

    **91.** Vitamin C in Juices ........................................................................335

# To the Student

Doing experiments in the laboratory is a chance to learn how chemistry actually works and to discover new things. In order to make the most of your laboratory experience you will need to prepare thoroughly before coming to the laboratory. To help you in your preparations we have designed **Prelaboratory Questions** to help you focus on the most important aspects of the experiment. One of the most important skills for you to learn in the laboratory is to record your data and observations during your experiment in an organized manner. The **Report Sheets** in this book are designed to help you do this. We have presented the **Data/Observations** section of the Report Sheets in different styles for various experiments to provide examples for you. As you complete each experiment you should evaluate the style until you find one you like. You can then make use of this style when you have no Report Sheet for an experiment or when you are asked to keep a laboratory notebook in later courses. Once you have completed the actual experiment you will need to analyze and summarize your results. To help you learn to do this efficiently, we have included **Analysis and Conclusions** questions and calculations. These are presented in a logical sequence, so you can come to appropriate conclusions about your experiment. We have also designed summary tables and graphs to show you how to organize your results so that you can more easily share them with others.

We hope you fill find the experiments interesting and the Report Sheets useful in organizing your data and conclusions as you explore the *World of Chemistry*. Have a great year!

S.S. Zumdahl
S.L. Zumdahl
D.J. DeCoste

# Safety in the Chemistry Laboratory

The chemistry laboratory is a place to experiment and learn. You will be working with equipment and materials that can harm if they are improperly handled. You must assume responsibility for your own safety and the safety of others working near you in the laboratory. Accidents most often happen in the carelessness, haste, and not following safety rules. You can help prevent accidents by closely following the instructions in your experiment and given by your teacher.

Safety rules for the laboratory are listed in the **Laboratory Safety Agreement**. Before beginning any work in the laboratory study these rules. When working in the lab, follow the rules at all times. If you have any questions about the rules, ask your teacher before starting lab work.

# First Aid in the Laboratory

**Report all accidents, injuries, and spills to your teacher immediately**.

**Be sure you know:**

- Safe laboratory techniques for your experiment
- Where and how to report an accident, injury, or spill
- The location of first-aid equipment, fire alarm, phone, eye washes, safety shower, fire extinguisher, fire blanket
- Evacuation procedures

| Injury | Safe Response |
|---|---|
| Burns | Flush with cool water. Call your teacher immediately. |
| Cuts and Bruises | Wash the cut with clean water. Call your teacher immediately. |
| Severe Bleeding | Apply pressure or a compress directly to the wound. Call your teacher immediately. |
| Fainting | Provide the person with fresh air. Call your teacher immediately. Have the person recline so that their head is lower than the rest of the body. |
| Fire | Remove the source of oxygen from the fire. For a container fire, place a cover on the container. For a person on fire, wrap him/her in a fire blanket. Call your teacher immediately. |
| Foreign matter in eye | Use the eyewash to flush the eye with lots of water. Be sure to keep the eye open. Call your teacher immediately. |
| Spills on skin | Flush with plenty of water or use the safety shower. Call your teacher. |
| Acid Spills | If a small spill, dilute with water and wipe up immediately. If a larger spill, apply baking soda, $NaHCO_3$, and call your teacher. |
| Base spills | If a small spill, dilute with water and wipe up immediately. If a larger spill, apply boric acid, $H_2BO_3$, and call your teacher. |

# Laboratory Safety Agreement

I,_____, have read and understand the following safety agreement. I agree to comply with all of the safety rules and guidelines stated below. Furthermore, I agree to follow any additional printed or verbal instructions given by my teacher or supervising adult during the school year.

1.  Be prepared to work in the laboratory. Read the experiment before coming to class and complete the prelaboratory assignment.

2.  Perform the experiments as directed. Do not do anything that is not part of an approved experimental procedure.

3.  **Never work without adult supervision**.

4.  Dress appropriately for lab.
    a.  Clothes should not be loose or floppy, especially in the sleeves.
    b.  Dangling necklaces or bracelets should be removed for lab.
    c.  Tie back long hair to keep it away from flames and chemicals.
    d.  Wear shoes that cover the entire foot.
    e.  Avoid wearing contact lenses.

5.  Wear appropriate protective equipment. Safety goggles and a lab apron or coat must be worn at all times. Gloves may be needed to protect your hands.

6.  Learn the location and operation of emergency equipment. This includes eye washes, safety showers, fire extinguishers, fire blankets, sinks, and first aid supplies. Know what to do in case of an emergency.

7.  Act in a responsible manner at all times. No horseplay or fooling around in the lab is allowed at anytime.

8.  Do not eat or drink in the laboratory.

9.  Never taste a chemical. Check odors only if instructed to do so, by gently wafting some of the vapor toward your nose with your hand. Be sure your work area is well ventilated for your experiment.

10. Turn off your Bunsen burner or other heat source whenever you are not using it. Never leave it unattended.

11. Keep all combustible material away from open flames.

12. Read chemical labels very carefully. Read them when you pick the bottle up, just before you use the chemical, and after you are finished measuring the chemical.

13. Report all accidents, injuries, and close calls to your teacher immediately.

14. Dispose of chemicals properly. No solid material goes down the drain. This includes burned matches. When solutions are disposed of down the drain, use plenty of water dilute the chemicals.

15. Never return used reagents to reagent bottles. Be careful to take just the amount you need. Do not contaminate the reagents.

16. Clean up the spills immediately. This includes water! Wash off chemicals splashed or spilled on your skin immediately and notify your teacher.

17. Treat all chemicals with respect. Know the hazards before you handle any chemical.

18. Clean up your work area. Put away all equipment and reagents and wash your hands thoroughly before leaving the laboratory.

19. List your allergies at the bottom of this Safety Agreement. If the experiment you are doing involves a substance you are allergic to, consult your teacher immediately.

I agree to follow all established safety rules and to work only under supervision of an adult.

Student signature_____ Date _____

Parent/Guardian signature_____ Date_____

Name_____

Section_____ Date_____

# Report for Experiment 1

## Chemistry of Fire

### Prelaboratory Questions

1.  Label the Bunsen burner parts shown below.

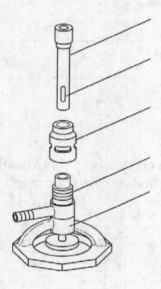

2.  What is the proper color for a burner flame?


### Data/Observations

**Part 1    Use of the Burner**

1.  Draw a copper wire within the flame.  Indicate the color of the copper wire at several places within the flame:

# Report for Experiment 1

Name_____

**Part 2     Efficiency of the Bunsen Burner**

Record the information from each of the five trials in the table below:

| Trial | Volume of water | Height of beaker over burner | Temp Reading 1 | Temp Reading 2 | Temp Reading 3 | Temp Reading 4 | Temp Reading 5 |
|-------|-----------------|------------------------------|----------------|----------------|----------------|----------------|----------------|
| 1 | | | | | | | |
| 2 | | | | | | | |
| 3 | | | | | | | |
| 4 | | | | | | | |
| 5 | | | | | | | |

# Analysis and Conclusions

1. Make a graph of temperature versus time.  Plot time on the *x*-axis (horizontal) and temperature on the *y*-axis (vertical). Place the plots for all of the trials on the same graph.  Label each line with the height of the beaker above the burner.

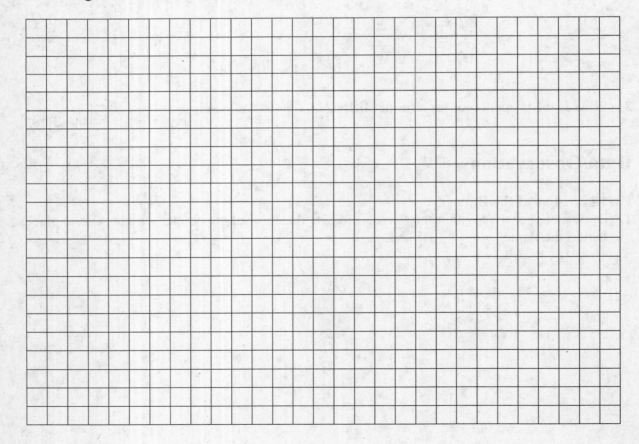

# Report for Experiment 1

Name_____

2. Which line shows the most efficient heating of the water? Explain why you chose this line.

3. What are the advantages of using a blue flame, instead of a yellow one, for heating objects in the laboratory?

4. Where is the hottest part of the blue flame?

5. When heating a substance over a Bunsen burner, where should the object be placed for most efficient heating? Why?

6. How does graphing the data help to determine the most efficient height for heating a liquid in a beaker?

Name_____

Section_____ Date_____

# Report for Experiment 2

## Scientific Observations

### Prelaboratory Questions

1. Which of the following statements is *not* a scientific observation? For those that are not observations, briefly explain why they are not.
   a. The wire is 18 cm long.

   b. The solution is blue-green in color.

   c. The reaction is producing a red-brown solid. It must be rust.

   d. The gas is being produced at a rate of 6.5 mL/second.

2. What distinguishes an observation from a conclusion?

### Data/Observations

Observations made before the experiment begins:

1.

2.

3.

4.

Observations made in procedure step 1.

# Report for Experiment 2

Name_____

Observations made in procedure step 3.

Observations made in procedure step 4.

Observations made following the conclusion of the experiment.

## Analysis and Conclusions

1. Do your observations from procedure step 1 indicate a chemical reaction? Explain.

2. Do your observations from procedure step 3 indicate a chemical reaction? Explain.

3. Do your observations from procedure step 4 indicate a chemical reaction? Explain.

4. What are some clues that a chemical reaction has taken place?

5. Identify the three qualitative observations you made that you think are most noticeable. Were any of your observations quantitative? If so, which?

# Report for Experiment 2

6. Classify each of your observations as qualitative or quantitative.




7. Is dissolving a solid in water a chemical reaction? Why or why not?




8. Is a metal disappearing into a solution a chemical reaction? Why or why not?




## Something Extra

1. Design an experiment that would separate the blue-green chemical from the water.



2. What name is given to chemical reactions which produce energy as heat? What are those reactions that consume energy as heat called?

# Report for Experiment 3

## Observations and Explanations

### Data/Observations

**Part I:**

1. Make a list of observations of the burning candle.

**Part II:**

2. What happens to the flame when the candle is covered?

3. How long does it take for the flame to almost go out after the candle is covered?

4. What happens to the flame when you lift the glass?

5. How long does it take for the flame to go out after the candle is covered again?

**Part III:**

6. Do you observe anything on the inside of the glass?  Discuss.

7. What happens to the flame when you lower the glass over the candle?

# Report for Experiment 3

Name_____

## Analysis and Conclusions

1. Compare your list of observations from Part I with another group of students. Which observations did you make that they did not? Which observations did they make that you did not?

2. Compare the times from questions 3 and 5 in the Data/Observations section.

3. Develop a theory that explains your observations when the candle is covered with the glass. Make sure to address the following.
   a. Support your theory with specific observations.
   b. How does your theory explain the differences in times when covering the candle (in Part II)?
   c. No theories answer all questions. What are two questions that your theory does not answer or address?

4. Why does a flame burn? Explain how your observations support your answer.

# Report for Experiment 3

5.  What is the difference between a theory and an observation? Give an example of each from this experiment.

## Something Extra

A few hundred years ago (before oxygen was discovered) scientists proposed a theory of burning that relied on a substance called phlogiston. In this theory, substances that burned were said to contain phlogiston. Burning resulted in the release of phlogiston, a substance that could not burn. Thus, the flame of a burning candle placed under a glass will eventually go out because the glass will become filled with phlogiston. Design an experiment to disprove the theory of phlogiston.

# Report for Experiment 4

## Physical and Chemical Changes

### Data/Observations

1. Make a list of observations for Part 1 of the experiment.

2. Make a list of observations for Part 2 of the experiment.

3. Make a list of observations for Part 3 of the experiment.

4. Make a list of observations for Part 4 of the experiment.

# Report for Experiment 4

**Name**_____

## Analysis and Conclusions

1. Fill in the table provided below. Discuss whether each change is physical or chemical with your lab partner. Record your conclusions in the table. Justify each choice below the table.

|  | Clues that a chemical change occurred | Chemical or physical change? |
|---|---|---|
| Food coloring to water |  |  |
| Mixing two solutions |  |  |
| Boiling water |  |  |
| Adding Mg to HCl |  |  |

Justify your choices for each Part (as either a physical or chemical change).

Part 1:

Part 2:

Part 3:

Part 4:

# Report for Experiment 4

Name_____

**2.** Do any of the procedures give a clue that a chemical change occurred, but are not chemical changes? Which ones?

**3.** What was the purpose of the sponge in Part 3? How did it help you decide if the process was a physical or chemical change?

**4.** Make microscopic drawings of each of the four processes. Discuss how these explain your observations.

**5.** Develop definitions of chemical change and physical change using atoms and molecules in your definitions.

## Something Extra

Chemists have learned that a chemical change always includes a rearrangement of the ways in which atoms are grouped. Explain what this statement means and discuss whether your observations support this statement.

Name_____

Section_____ Date_____

# Report for Experiment 5

## Household Chemistry

### Prelaboratory Questions

**1.** What is the difference between a physical and a chemical property?

**2.** List three clues used to tell whether a chemical reaction has occurred.

### Data/Observations

| Solid | Color | Reaction with water | Reaction with vinegar | Reaction with iodine solution |
|---|---|---|---|---|
| **Pure solids** | | | | |
| 1 Salt | | | | |
| 2 Baking soda | | | | |
| 3 Baking powder | | | | |
| 4 Starch | | | | |
| 5 Sugar | | | | |
| **Mixtures (2 solids)** | | | | |
| Mixture 1 | | | | |
| Mixture 2 | | | | |
| **Unknown Mixture** | | | | |
| Mixture 3 | | | | |

# Report for Experiment 5

Name_____

## Analysis and Conclusions

1.  Compare your data for the pure substances with the data for each of the two solid mixtures. Which of the pure substances shows behavior that is similar to what you saw with the two-solid mixtures, Mixture 1 and Mixture 2. If you cannot positively identify your mixture, discuss the possibilities for the mixtures.

2.  Compare your results for the unknown mixture (Mixture 3) to the observed characteristics of each pure substance. Can you identify any of the pure substances as a component of the unknown? Explain.

# Report for Experiment 5

3. Based on your answer to question 1, what is the identity for each of your two-solid mixtures?

   Mixture 1 is _____ and _____.

   Mixture 2 is _____ and _____.

4. What is the major component of the unknown (Mixture 3), commonly used as an upset-stomach and pain reliever)?  Compare your results to the ingredients on the package.

5. Two of the pure substances (baking powder and baking soda) are used to make baked products. What chemical property makes these substances useful in baking?  How is this property useful in baking?  Which two of the five pure substances exhibit this property?

6. Baking soda reacts with acidic solutions, but not with water.  Identify which of the 5 pure compounds is baking soda and which is baking powder.  Explain.

# Report for Experiment 5

Name_____

7. One of your pure substances produced a characteristic color (blue-black) when it reacted with the iodine-alcohol solution. Starch is an organic compound you probably encountered in your biology course. Identify which of the pure substances is starch.

## Something Extra

What property do the upset-stomach reliever and the baking ingredients have in common? Give a hypothesis for how this property could possibly produce relief for an upset stomach.

Name_____

Section_____ Date_____

# Report for Experiment 6

## Properties of Matter

### Prelaboratory Questions

1. No food or drink should ever be brought into or consumed in the laboratory. Why not?


2. As the procedure describes, you should never test the odor of a reagent by holding it directly under your nose. Why not?


### Data/Observations   (add paper, if needed.)

| Substance Tested | Physical State | Odor/Appearance | Flammable? (Y/N) | Other Notes |
|---|---|---|---|---|
| | | | | |
| | | | | |
| | | | | |
| | | | | |
| | | | | |
| | | | | |
| | | | | |
| | | | | |

# Report for Experiment 6

Name_____

| Substance Tested | Physical State | Odor/Appearance | Flammable? (Y/N) | Other Notes |
|---|---|---|---|---|
|  |  |  |  |  |
|  |  |  |  |  |
|  |  |  |  |  |
|  |  |  |  |  |
|  |  |  |  |  |
|  |  |  |  |  |

## Analysis and Conclusions

**Summarize** your findings, including (but not limited to) the following suggestions:

- **Categorize** the samples into groups that show similarities. Clearly identify the reasons behind your groupings.

- What **generalizations** can you make about: solubilities? ability to conduct electric currents? flammability?

- Discuss any **further tests** that might have given you more information about the various samples.

# Report for Experiment 7

## Separation Challenge

### Prelaboratory Questions

1. List four separation techniques that might be used in this experiment. Explain how each could isolate a component of the mixture.

2. Draw a flow chart to show how you would proceed to isolate each component in your sample.

# Report for Experiment 7

Name_____

## Analysis and Conclusions

Your report should include the following components:

1. Statement of purpose.

2. A list of materials used.

3. Your procedure written in a series of numbered steps.

4. A discussion of your sources of error in both your separation and recovery techniques. Explain how you might proceed differently in the future to eliminate these problems.

5. Use a piece of cardboard (8 ½ in x 11 in) to create a flow chart for your procedure. Attach the baggies containing your separated sample to the proper places on the chart. Label it with your name and turn it in to your teacher.

6. The physical properties of the substances to be separated are the essential key to a successful separation. Separation techniques are based on these physical properties.

   Explain how these statements relate to your challenge. Give several specific examples from your procedure of the property and the separation achieved.

# Report for Experiment 8

## The Sludge Test

### Prelaboratory Questions

**1.** Explain how a filtration can separate a substance that dissolves from one that does not dissolve. In this experiment what does filtration separate?

**2.** What techniques are needed to isolate the salt in this experiment?

# Report for Experiment 8

Name_____

## Data/Observations

### Data Table

| | |
|---|---|
| Mass of sludge resource material | _____g |
| Mass of beaker 1 | _____g |
| Mass of beaker 1 and sludge resource material | _____g |
| Mass of filter paper | _____g |
| Mass of filter paper and sand | _____g |
| Mass of sand | _____g |
| Mass of gravel | _____g |
| Mass of beaker 2 | _____g |
| Mass of beaker 2 and salt | _____g |
| Mass of salt | _____g |

## Analysis and Conclusions

1. Determine the mass of each component in the sludge mixture and record it in the Summary Table.

2. Determine the percent by mass of each component in the mixture. Show a calculation for one of the components below. Record the percent for each component in the Summary Table.

# Report for Experiment 8

Name_____

## Summary Table

| Sludge Component | Mass | Percent of Mixture |
|---|---|---|
| Gravel | | |
| Sand | | |
| Salt | | |

3. Would heating the sludge to begin the separation have been an alternative method for separating the mixture? Explain.

4. Why is it important to avoid spattering the salt solution during the evaporation process?

5. What are possible sources for error in your results?

Name_____

6.  Obtain the true composition of the sludge from your teacher.  Discuss how well your results match the true composition of the mixture and the results obtained by other groups.

## Something Extra

Propose an alternative method for separating the gravel from the sludge mixture.

Name_____

Section_____ Date_____

# Report for Experiment 9

## Separation of Mixtures

## Prelaboratory Questions

1. Write a one-sentence explanation of what is meant by a *volatile* substance.

2. Describe the correct procedure for testing the odors of unknown substances.

3. What physical property will make it possible for you to collect one of the mixture components by extraction?

4. If you heat a mixture containing one or more volatile components, what is likely to happen?

## Data and Observations

### Table 1

| | |
|---|---|
| Mass of stoppered reaction tube and original sample: | _____ g |
| Mass of Erlenmeyer flask and boiling stone: | _____ g |
| Mass of filter paper: | _____ g |
| Mass of empty reaction tube and stopper: | _____ g |
| Mass of Erlenmeyer flask, boiling stone, and soluble residue: | _____ g |
| Mass of filter paper and insoluble residue: | _____ g |

# Report for Experiment 9

Name_____

## Table 2

Appearance of original mixture:

Temperature change during dissolving:

Appearance of insoluble solid:

Appearance of residue in reaction tube:

## Table 3      Summary of Results

Show your calculations in the space below each item.

Mass of original sample:                                        _____ g

Mass of insoluble residue:                                     _____ g

Mass of soluble residue:                                        _____ g

Total mass of recovered solids:                            _____ g

Percent of original sample recovered:                 _____ %

Percent of original sample left after extraction:   _____ %
("soluble residue")

Percent of original sample recovered by evaporation:   _____ %
("insoluble residue")

Percent of original sample "lost":                        _____ %

# Report for Experiment 9

Name_____

## Analysis and Conclusions

1. How does the appearance of each of the recovered solids compare with the original mixture? Be complete. Note that you are being asked to make three comparisons, not just one.

2. How many of the three components of the original mixture must have been in the liquid extract? Defend your answer.

3. Consult with at least three other groups. How do their results for percent of material recovered compare with yours?

4. Account for the material "lost" during the experiment. In what part of the procedure was it most likely lost? (**Hint:** Recall the discussion of "volatile" substances in the introduction and in the prelaboratory questions.)

# Report for Experiment 9

**Name_____**

## Something Extra

The answers to these questions are based on the results obtained by the class as a whole.

1. Enter your values for the percent by mass of the insoluble residue and the soluble residue in the Class Data Table, as directed by your teacher. Also enter the percent of original sample that was "lost" during the experiment.

2. Calculate the mean (average) values for the percentages of soluble and insoluble residue, as well as the mean value for percentage lost.

   Soluble residue: _____%

   Insoluble residue: _____%

   Material lost: _____%

3. Calculate the average percent deviations for each of the three fractions.

   Soluble residue: ±_____%

   Insoluble residue: ±_____%

   Material lost: ±_____%

4. Examine the three percentages and their deviations.
   a. What is the sum of the three percentages? Ideally, what should the sum be? Why?

# Report for Experiment 9

Name_____

**b.** Suggest one or more reasons why the sum of the percentages might be different from what you predicted in 4a. Based on your reasons, would the sum of the individual percentages be more likely to be greater than 100% or less than 100%. Explain.

**c.** By how much might you expect the sum of the percentages to differ from 100%? By 1%? By 5%? By 10%? Discuss.

**d.** Discuss the precision of this experiment and make suggestions as to where the procedure might be changed so that all of the groups would report similar results.

Name_____

Section_____ Date_____

# Report for Experiment 10

## Distillation

## Prelaboratory Questions

1. Why is it important that the distilling flask not be allowed to go to dryness?

2. Why is it important to place the tip of the temperature probe well below the sidearm of the distilling flask? (**Hint:** What temperature is it supposed to be measuring?)

3. What is the function of the ice water in the beaker that holds the receiver vial?

4. Would distillation be a satisfactory means of separating a liquid from a dissolved solid? Explain.

## Data/Observations

### Data Table 1        The Distillation

Temperature at first sign of boiling:                                    _____ ° C

Temperature when refluxing is first observed:                    _____ ° C

# Report for Experiment 10

Name_____

## Data Table 2     Comparison of Properties

### A. Appearance and Odor

Appearance of original mixture:

Odor of original mixture:

Appearance of distillate:

Odor of distillate:

### B. Density of Distillate

Volume of distillate recovered:

Mass of graduate and distillate:

Mass of clean, dry graduate:

Density of distillate (show calculations below):

### C. Flammability Tests

Original mixture:

Distillate:

Residue from distilling flask:

# Report for Experiment 10

Name_____

**D. Cobalt(II) Chloride Tests**

Color of original mixture with $CoCl_2$ _____

Color of distillate with $CoCl_2$ _____

Color of residue in flask with $CoCl_2$ _____

## Analysis and Conclusions

1. Use Graph Link to transfer the graph of temperature vs. time to a computer. Print the graph and attach it to this report.

2. Use the TRACE button on your calculator to trace along the graph as it appears on the screen. On the graph, indicate the following:
   a. The temperature at which you began recording.
   b. The time at which the graph began its steep rise.
   c. The time and temperature when the graph began to level.
   d. The temperature range during the time when most of the distillate was recovered.

3. In the space below, give a *written* description of the shape of your graph.

4. a. How did the flammability of the distillate compare with that of the residue left in the distilling flask and of the original mixture of methanol and water? Is it possible to distinguish among the three liquids on the basis of flammability? Explain.

   b. Summarize your findings when each of the three liquid fractions was tested with cobalt(II) chloride. Is it possible to distinguish among the three using the results of these tests? Explain.

# Report for Experiment 10     Name_____

5. During distillation, the temperature of the escaping liquid remains relatively constant while most of the liquid distills. This temperature is the boiling point of the distillate.

   a. At what temperature did most of the methanol distill in your experiment? _____ °C

   b. How does this temperature compare with the accepted boiling point of pure methanol, which is 65°C?

   c. What can you conclude about the identity of the liquid left in the flask?

## Something Extra

1. In addition to the flammability and cobalt chloride tests, density can also help in identification of an unknown liquid. Use data from your experiment to determine the density of your distillate. The accepted value for the density of methanol is 0.791 g/mL. Determine the percent deviation between your experimental value for the density of the distillate and the accepted value. (Divide the deviation between the values by the accepted value. Convert the resulting decimal fraction to a percent.)

2. Originally, you set up the CBL to use stored calibration data. Discuss the value of carrying out a manual calibration, rather than using stored data. How might you conduct such a calibration? In what sort of experimental situations might it be preferable to manually calibrate the CBL instead of relying on stored data?

Name_____

Section_____ Date_____

# Report for Experiment 11

## Aluminum Atoms

### Prelaboratory Questions

1.  What measurements will you need in order to determine the thickness of a piece of aluminum foil?

### Data/Observations

#### Data Table

Mass of aluminum block _____ g

Volume of water in graduated cylinder _____ mL

Volume of water with aluminum block _____ mL

Aluminum foil

    Width _____ cm

    Length _____ cm

Mass of aluminum foil _____ g

# Report for Experiment 11

Name_____

## Analysis and Conclusions

1. Calculate the volume of the aluminum block from the apparent change in the volume of the water in the cylinder.

2. Since both the aluminum block and the aluminum foil are pure elemental aluminum, we would expect the ratio of the mass to the volume to be the same for both. That is:

$$\frac{\text{mass of block}}{\text{volume of block}} = \frac{\text{mass of foil}}{\text{volume of foil}}$$

Use this relationship to find the volume of the aluminum foil.

3. Calculate the thickness of the aluminum foil. (**Hint:** Think about how you would calculate the volume of a box from its measurement. Think of the piece of aluminum foil as a very thin box.)

# Report for Experiment 11

**Name**_____

4.  One aluminum atom has a diameter of 0.000000025 cm. How many atoms thick is the aluminum foil?

5.  What are the possible sources for error in your experiment?

## Something Extra

Look up the diameters for lithium, sodium, potassium and cesium atoms. What is the relationship between the atomic number of the element and the diameter of its atoms?

# Report for Experiment 12

## Electrolysis

### Prelaboratory Questions

1. Suggest an explanation for the green indicator color before the electrolysis begins. Remember that distilled water and sodium sulfate are neither acidic nor basic (see Introduction).

2. Write the formula for water. Write the formulas for the new substances formed in this experiment. Be sure to include the physical states for all substances.

### Data/Observations

Evidence for a chemical change:

# Report for Experiment 12

Name_____

## Analysis and Conclusions

1. There are ample clues for chemical (as well as physical) changes in the process which you have just carried out. Cite at least three indicators of chemical change that you observed in this experiment.

2. Following the completion of your portion of the experiment, your teacher performed two demonstrations which illustrated important characteristics of the products of the decomposition.
   a. What does the 'rocket launch' tell you about a mixture of hydrogen and oxygen gases?

   b. In the second demonstration, for which the plastic pipet bulb was clamped in place, why did the bulb fill with water? What difference between gases and liquids does this illustrate?

# Report for Experiment 13

## Classifying Elements

### Prelaboratory Questions

1. Consult the periodic table on the inside back cover of your text. Based on the elements you are familiar with, where are most of the metals found?

2. Look at the numbering system for the groups as explained in Chapter 3 of your textbook. Do the "A" groups contain mostly metals or mostly nonmetals? Do the groups in the middle of the table, (transition elements) contain mostly metals or mostly nonmetals?

3. What basis did Mendeleev use to divide the elements into **groups**?

### Data/Observations

**Data Table**

| Element | Malleable or Brittle? | Conducts? | Shiny or Dull? | Color or Other Characteristics |
|---------|----------------------|-----------|----------------|-------------------------------|
| a |  |  |  |  |
| b |  |  |  |  |
| c |  |  |  |  |
| d |  |  |  |  |
| e |  |  |  |  |
| f |  |  |  |  |
| g |  |  |  |  |
| h |  |  |  |  |

# Report for Experiment 13    Name_____

## Analysis and Conclusions

1. For each of the five tests of physical and chemical properties, separate the eight elements according to their behavior on that particular test. Place the letter of each element in the space below the descriptions that fit.

### A. Physical Properties

| Malleable | Shiny | Conducts |
|---|---|---|
|  |  |  |
| **Brittle** | **Dull** | **Nonconducting** |
|  |  |  |

### B. Chemical Properties

| reacts with HCl(*aq*) | reacts with CuCl$_2$(*aq*) |
|---|---|
|  |  |
| **unreactive with HCl(*aq*)** | **unreactive with CuCl$_2$(*aq*):** |
|  |  |

2. Combine your five pairs of lists from Question 1 into two groups of elements such that all the members of a given group are alike in at least most of the properties tested. You may find that you have one or two elements that don't clearly belong to either of your two categories because some properties fit one group while other properties fit the second group better. If that happens, make them a third category.

| Category 1 | Category 2 | Category 3 (?) |
|---|---|---|
|  |  |  |

# Report for Experiment 13

Name_____

3. Describe briefly the criteria you used to make your groupings. Identify any difficulties you encountered in deciding where to place each element.

4. Using the definitions for metals, nonmetals and metalloids from your textbook, and your groupings, try to identify each of the elements **a** through **h** as being a *metal*, a *nonmetal*, or a *metalloid*.

| Element | A | B | C | D | E | F | G | H |
|---|---|---|---|---|---|---|---|---|
| Classification | | | | | | | | |

# Report for Experiment 14

## Electric Solutions

### Prelaboratory Questions

1. Why does the bulb light? What does it mean if the bulb doesn't light?

2. Why did we add nothing to a beaker of water and test it?

### Data/Observations

1. Record your observations in the table below.

| Name | Did the bulb light? |
|---|---|
| water | |
| table sugar | |
| sodium chloride | |
| potassium nitrate | |
| HCl | |
| vinegar | |

2. What happens when water is added to the solutions that originally caused the bulb to light?

# Report for Experiment 14     Name_____

## Analysis and Conclusions

1. How are the compounds similar that caused the bulb to light?

2. True or false: The reason a compound did not cause the bulb to light is because the substance did not dissolve in water. Explain your answer.

3. What do your observations tell you about the contents of each cup? Draw molecular level pictures for each cup to explain your results.

4. Explain what happened when you added water to the solutions that originally caused the bulb to light by using molecular level pictures.

5. How could we tell if a compound consisted of ions if it does not dissolve in water?

## Something Extra

Test several household products to see if they contain ions. Get permission from your teacher first.

# Report for Experiment 15

## Forming and Naming Ionic Compounds

### Prelaboratory Questions

1.  For the following pairs of ions, write the formula of the compound that you would expect them to form:
    a. barium and hydroxide

    b. cobalt (III) and phosphate

    c. iron (II) and sulfate

    d. silver and hydrogen carbonate

2.  Platinum is a transition metal and forms $Pt^{2+}$ and $Pt^{4+}$ ions. Write the formulas for the compounds for each of these ions with
    a.  bromide ions

    b.  carbonate ions.

### Data/Observations

| | $Na_3PO_4$ $PO_4^{3-}$ | KOH $OH^-$ | $K_4Fe(CN)_6$ $Fe(CN)_6^{4-}$ | $Na_2CO_3$ $CO_3^{2-}$ | KI $I^-$ | $Na_2 C_2O_4$ $C_2O_4^{2-}$ |
|---|---|---|---|---|---|---|
| $CoCl_2$ $Co^{2+}$ | | | | | | |
| $Pb(NO_3)_2$ $Pb^{2+}$ | | | | | | |
| $CuSO_4$ $Cu^{2+}$ | | | | | | |
| $Fe(NO_3)_3$ $Fe^{3+}$ | | | | | | |
| $NiCl_2$ $Ni^{2+}$ | | | | | | |
| $SrCl_2$ $Sr^{2+}$ | | | | | | |
| $AgNO_3$ $Ag^+$ | | | | | | |

# Report for Experiment 15

Name_____

## Analysis and Conclusions

1. For each case in which you found a reaction occurred, write the correct formula for the substance formed.

| | $Na_3PO_4$ $PO_4^{3-}$ | KOH $OH^-$ | $K_4Fe(CN)_6$ $Fe(CN)_6^{4-}$ | $Na_2CO_3$ $CO_3^{2-}$ | KI $I^-$ | $Na_2 C_2O_4$ $C_2O_4^{2-}$ |
|---|---|---|---|---|---|---|
| $CoCl_2$ $Co^{2+}$ | | | | | | |
| $Pb(NO_3)_2$ $Pb^{2+}$ | | | | | | |
| $CuSO_4$ $Cu^{2+}$ | | | | | | |
| $Fe(NO_3)_3$ $Fe^{3+}$ | | | | | | |
| $NiCl_2$ $Ni^{2+}$ | | | | | | |
| $SrCl_2$ $Sr^{2+}$ | | | | | | |
| $AgNO_3$ $Ag^+$ | | | | | | |

2. For each formula write the correct chemical name for the compound formed.

# Report for Experiment 16

## Grocery Store Nomenclature

### Summary Table

Fill in the table below.

| | Chemical name | Chemical formula | Justification | Products containing this chemical |
|---|---|---|---|---|
| 1. | | | | |
| 2. | | | | |
| 3. | | | | |
| 4. | | | | |
| 5. | | | | |

### Something Extra

Contact a company that produces a product that contains one of the chemicals on your list and find out the purpose of the chemical in the product.

Name_____

Section_____ Date_____

# Report for Experiment 17

## Energy Changes In Physical and Chemical Systems

### Prelaboratory Questions

1. What distinguishes a physical change from a chemical change?


2. When something feels cold to the touch, in what direction is energy being transferred to or from your body?

### Data/Observations

**Part 1**


**Part 2**


### Analysis and Conclusions

**Part 1    Calcium Chloride and Water**

1.  a.  When you touched the cylinder after adding water to the calcium chloride, was energy being released or absorbed by the contents? Explain.


    b.  Was energy being released or absorbed by your hand? Explain.

# Report for Experiment 17

Name_____

**Part 2    Vinegar and Baking Soda**

**1. a.** What evidence do you have that something new is being formed in this case?

**b.** When you touched the cylinder, was energy being released or absorbed by the contents. Explain.

**c.** Was energy being released or absorbed by your hand? Explain.

**2.** Any process that releases energy is said to be *exothermic*. Any process that takes in (absorbs energy) is described as being *endothermic*.

**a.** When calcium chloride, $CaCl_2$ dissolves in water is the process exothermic or endothermic? Explain.

**b.** Is the reaction between baking soda, (sodium bicarbonate, $NaHCO_3$), and vinegar, (dilute acetic acid, $HC_2H_3O_2$), exothermic or endothermic? Explain.

Name_____

Section_____ Date_____

# Report for Experiment 18

## Measurement and the SI System

### Prelaboratory Questions

1. If you are using a graduated cylinder for which the smallest division is 0.1 mL, to what degree of precision should you report liquid volumes?  Express your answer in the form:

$$\pm \text{ (uncertainty)  mL}$$

2. A stack of five 3.5-inch floppy disks is 1.6 cm tall.
   a. What is the average thickness of one disk?

   b. To the nearest whole number, how many disks will be in a stack 10 cm tall?

3. In Celsius degrees:
   a. What is the boiling point of water?           _____ °C

   b. What is the freezing point of water?           _____ °C

   c. What is normal human body temperature?           _____ °C

4. What is a meniscus; what role does it play in the correct reading of liquid volumes?

### Data/Observations
**Table 1-A**

| Graduated Cylinder | Nominal Capacity | Volume of Liquid |
|---|---|---|
| 1 | | |
| 2 | | |
| 3 | | |
| 4 | | |
| 5 | | |
| 6 | | |

# Report for Experiment 18

Name_____

| Table 1 – B | | |
|---|---|---|
| Cylinder | | Uncertainty |
| 1 | ± | mL |
| 2 | ± | mL |
| 3 | ± | mL |
| 4 | ± | mL |
| 5 | ± | mL |
| 6 | ± | mL |

| Table 2 | |
|---|---|
| **Volume of liquid in:** | |
| 25-mL graduate | _____ mL |
| 100-mL graduate | _____ mL |

| Table 3 |
|---|
| Diameter of penny: _____ cm _____ mm |
| Diameter of nickel: _____ cm _____ mm |
| Number of pennies in 1-cm stack: _____ |
| Mass of 1-cm stack: _____ g ± _____ g |

| Table 4 |
|---|
| Mass of pre-1982 penny: _____ g |
| Mass of post-1982 penny: _____ g |

| Table 5 |
|---|
| Temperature of ice-water mixture: _____ °C |
| Temperature of ice-salt-water mixture: _____ °C |

# Report for Experiment 18      Name_____

## Analysis and Conclusions

1. It is common to get different volume readings from each container in Part 2. What explanation can you offer for:
   a. An apparent decrease in volume?


   b. An apparent increase in volume?


2. Which container in Part 2 gave you the most *precise* reading of the actual volume of water it held? Justify your choice. (**Hint:** Remember the distinction between precision and accuracy given in the Introduction.)


3. The beaker you used in Part 2 probably carries the notation "± 5%." What do you interpret this to mean?


4. Calculate the average thickness of a single penny using the data you obtained in Part 3 of the procedure. Show your calculations in the space below.


5. Explain how you could estimate the mass of a large stack containing an unknown number of pennies using only the data in Table 3.


6. Determine the number of pennies that could be laid edge-to-edge the full length of a meter stick. Repeat the calculation for nickels. (**Hint:** Have you ever seen a third of a penny? Do fractional coins exist?)

# Report for Experiment 18

Name_____

7. Compare your results from Part 4 with those of other teams. How do the masses of pennies minted before 1982 compare with the masses of newer ones? Try to explain the difference.

8. Errors or variations from expected results that *do not* result from carelessness or incorrect procedure are called *random experimental errors*. Experimental errors are no one's fault; they are unavoidable and they must be taken into account any time we evaluate the results of an experiment. Suggest two sources of random experimental errors that might cause different teams to get different results in Part 4 of the Procedure.

9. What effect does salt have on the temperature of an ice-water mixture? Did other groups observe the same effect?

Name_____

Section_____ Date_____

# Report for Experiment 19

## Measuring A Book?  Precisely!

### Analysis and Conclusions

1. Which ruler gives you the most precise measure of the perimeter and area of the cover of your chemistry textbook?  Why?

2. Which ruler gives you the least precise measure of the perimeter and area of the cover of your chemistry textbook?  Why?

3. Justify the number of significant figures in each of your measurements.

4. Justify the number of significant figures in each of your calculations.

# Report for Experiment 19     Name_____

5. Compare your measurements with other groups. For which ruler was there the most difference among groups? The least difference? Explain.

6. Compare your calculations with other groups. For which ruler was there the most difference among groups? The least difference? Explain.

## Summary Table
Record your measurements and calculations in the table below.

| Ruler # | length | width | length | width | perimeter | area |
|---------|--------|-------|--------|-------|-----------|------|
| 1 | ft | ft | cm | cm | cm | cm$^2$ |
| 2 | in | in | cm | cm | cm | cm$^2$ |
| 3 | cm | cm | cm | cm | cm | cm$^2$ |
| 4 | cm | cm | cm | cm | cm | cm$^2$ |

## Something Extra
For each ruler, what is the largest length that you can measure that you would report as a measurement of zero? Explain.

Name_____

Section_____ Date_____

# Report for Experiment 20

## Conversion Factors

### Prelaboratory Questions

**1.** Describe the procedure for determining the slope of a straight-line graph.

**2.** Explain the difference between a *measurement* and a *number*.

**3.** Every conversion factor can be written in two ways. Complete the table below.

| | |
|---|---|
| 7 days = 1 week | 1 day = 0.143 week ( 1 ÷ 7 = 0.143 ) |
| 12 inches = 1 foot | 1 inch = _____ foot |
| 100 cm = 1 m | 1 cm = _____ m |
| $1 = 10 dimes | 1 dime = $ _____ |

### Data/Observations

#### Table 1

| | |
|---|---|
| Mass of empty, dry graduated cylinder | _____ g |
| Mass of graduate + 1.50 mL distilled water | _____ g |
| Mass of graduate + 3.00 mL distilled water | _____ g |
| Mass of graduate + 5.00 mL distilled water | _____ g |
| Volume after 1st 20 drops is added | _____ mL |
| Volume after 2nd 20 drops is added | _____ mL |

# Report for Experiment 20

**Name**_____

## Analysis and Conclusions

1. Use the information in Table 1 to calculate the mass of water in 0.00 mL, 1.50 mL, 3.00 mL and 5.00 mL.  Show your calculations below and enter the results in Table 2.

### Table 2

| Volume of water | Mass of water |
|---|---|
| 0.00 mL | |
| 1.50 mL | |
| 3.00 mL | |
| 5.00 mL | |

2. Use the grid below to plot the data from Table 2.  Label the axes, with mass on the vertical axis and volume on the horizontal axis.  Draw the best-fit straight line through the four data points.

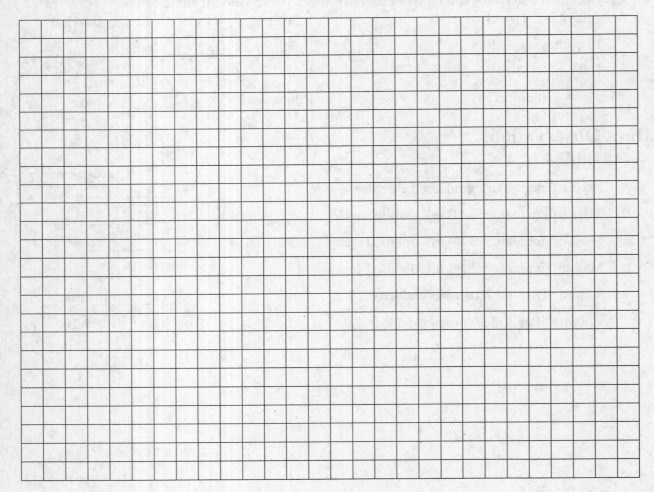

# Report for Experiment 20

Name_____

3. Use the space provided to show the results for **a** through **e**. Enter each result in Table 4.

   **a.** Graphing your data allows you to find values you didn't actually measure. Use your graph to find **(i)** the mass of 2.40 mL of water and **(ii)** the volume of 4.25 g of water.

   **b.** Calculate the *slope* of your graph. This is the density of water.

   **c.** Based on your results for steps 5 and 6 of the procedure (see Table 1), what is the average volume for the number of drops listed below:

   **Table 3**

   | Drops | Average Volume |
   |-------|----------------|
   | 20    |                |
   | 100   |                |
   | 50    |                |
   | 10    |                |
   | 1     |                |

   **d.** Use the density you determined for water to find:

   **(i)** the total mass of water in the graduate after the first 20-drop addition

   **(ii)** the total mass of water in the graduate after the second 20-drop addition.

   **(iii)** the average mass of 20 drops of water?

# Report for Experiment 20

Name_____

**e.** What is the mass of:

    **(i)** 1 drop of water?

    **(ii)** $10^6$ drops ?

    **(iii)** $6.02 \times 10^{23}$ drops?

## Table 4

| | |
|---|---|
| Mass of 2.40 mL of water | _____ g |
| Volume of 4.25 g of water | _____ mL |
| Density of water (from graph) | _____ g/mL |
| Average volume of 20 drops of water | _____ mL |
| Volume of 100 drops of water | _____ mL |
| Volume of 50 drops of water | _____ mL |
| Volume of 10 drops of water | _____ mL |
| Volume of 1 drop of water | _____ mL |
| Mass of water after 1st 20 drops | _____ g |
| Mass of water after 2nd 20 drops | _____ g |
| Average mass of 20 drops of water | _____ g |
| Mass of 1 drop of water | _____ g |
| Mass of $10^6$ drops of water | _____ g |
| Mass of $6.02 \times 10^{23}$ drops of water | _____ g |

# Report for Experiment 20

**Name**_____

4. Use your experimental results to complete the following conversions. Show calculations below.

    **a.** 1 drop of water = _____ g     = _____ mL

    **b.** 1 gram of water = _____ mL     = _____ drops

    **c.** 1 milliliter of water = _____ g     = _____ drops

5. If you did not start with a completely dry graduated cylinder in step 1, would this affect your answers? If so, what part of the answer would be incorrect: the mass of water, the volume of water, or both? Explain.

6. If the drops of water from the pipet hit the sides of the graduate, how could this affect your answers? Again, be specific in describing what can go wrong.

7. The density of water is often assumed to be exactly one gram per milliliter. How close to that value did the slope of your graph come? If your value was not within 5% of the accepted value, that is, within the range of 0.95 g/mL $\leq$ density $\leq$ 1.05 g/mL, was there anything about the procedure that made it difficult for you to get a precise result? Explain.

# Report for Experiment 20

**Name**_____

## Something Extra

1. The values obtained by the class for the density of water will be listed on the board. Use the posted information to calculate the mean value for water's density, the average deviation and percent deviation.

   a. The mean is simply the arithmetic average of all the individual results. Show calculation.

   Mean value for<br>density of water: _____

   b. Deviation refers to the difference between the mean and each individual value. Deviations are reported as absolute values, so do not include signs. Show two sample calculations of deviations, one for a value greater than the mean and one for a value less than the mean.

   c. As the name implies, the average deviation is the arithmetic mean of the individual deviations. Show your calculations.

   Average deviation:_____

   d. Combine your answers to 1(a) and 1(c) to express the experimental value for the density of water in the form (mean) ± (average deviation). Round both portions of the answer to the appropriate decimal place.

   Density of water: _____ ± _____ g/mL

2. Use your graphing calculator to determine both the mean value for the density of water and the standard deviation from that mean. Report the density of water in the form: (mean) ± (standard deviation). Round both portions of the answer to the appropriate number of decimal places.

   Density of water: _____ ± _____ g/mL

Name_____

Section_____ Date_____

# Report for Experiment 21

## Measurement and Density

### Prelaboratory Questions

1. Describe how to determine the limitation of a metric ruler.

2. Why is it important to read the graduated cylinder at eye level on the bench top?

3. Why is it important to be sure that no drops of water cling to the cylinder in the water displacement method?

## Data/Observations

### Summary Table

| Part 1 | Length | Width | Height | Volume | Mass | Density |
|--------|--------|-------|--------|--------|------|---------|
| Block 1 | | | | | | |
| Block 2 | | | | | | |
| Block 3 | | | | | | |

| Part 2 | Diameter | Height | Volume (water) | Volume(formula) |
|--------|----------|--------|----------------|-----------------|
| Beaker | | | | |

| | Irregular solid |
|--|--|
| **Volume of** | |
| Water alone | mL |
| Water + solid | mL |
| Solid alone | mL |
| Mass of solid | g |
| Density of solid | g/mL |

# Report for Experiment 21

Name_____

## Analysis and Conclusions

1. Density is the mass of an object in relation to the space it occupies.
   It is expressed as D = Mass/Volume.  Calculate the density of each of the blocks from
   Part 1 and record them in the Summary Table. Show an example calculation for one of the
   blocks below. Calculate the density of the irregular solid and record it in the Summary Table
   above.

2. Write the procedure you used to determine the density of the potato in a series of numbered
   steps.

3. Construct a data table for the potato density similar to those above.  Calculate the density of the
   potato.

4. How does the volume measured by water compare to the volume calculated by formula for the
   beaker?  Explain.

# Report for Experiment 21

Name_____

**5.** How do your volumes of the beaker in the question above compare to the stated volume of the beaker? Explain.

**6.** How would you determine the mass of a quantity of liquid?

**7.** How would you determine the volume of an irregular object that dissolves in water?

## Something Extra

**1.** Find the volume of each block you used in Part 1 by the water displacement method. Compare the volumes to those you found by using a mathematical formula in Part 2. Explain any differences.

**2.** Solid shortening sticks to the measuring cup making it difficult to measure accurately. Give an alternative method for measuring shortening using the skills from this experiment.

Name_____

Section_____ Date_____

# Report for Experiment 22

## The Bean Lab
### *An Investigation into Moles*

## Prelaboratory Questions

1. What number is represented by each of these names? Consult a dictionary for any that you do not recognize.

   a. score                    b. gross                    c. decade


   d. century                  e. ream (of paper)


2. How many objects are in each of the following?
   a. 7 dozen eggs             b. 0.25 ream of paper


3. A box is weighed, then filled with 100 glass marbles and weighed again. The marbles are removed and replaced with 100 plastic spheres; the box and spheres are weighed a final time. Explain how you would calculate the mass ratio of one glass marble to one plastic sphere.




## Observations and Data

1. Show a sample calculation for the mass of 50 beans (without the cup) in this space. Enter the result for all five types of beans in the Data Table for Part 1, next page.




2. Calculate the relative masses of each type of bean and record them in the data table below. Sample calculation of relative mass:

# Report for Experiment 22

**Name**_____

Data Table for Part 1          Mass of empty cup: _____ g

| Type of Bean | Symbol | Mass of cup and 50 beans | Mass of 50 beans alone | Relative Mass | Rank |
|---|---|---|---|---|---|
|  |  |  |  |  |  |
|  |  |  |  |  |  |
|  |  |  |  |  |  |
|  |  |  |  |  |  |
|  |  |  |  |  |  |

3. Enter the relative masses in the Data Table for Part 2, then carry out **Part 2** of the Procedure. We will define as one "pot," the nearest whole number of beans needed to get a mass in grams that is equal to the relative mass for that type of bean.

**Data Table for Part 2**

| Type of Bean | Symbol | Relative Mass | Number in 1 Pot |
|---|---|---|---|
|  |  |  |  |
|  |  |  |  |
|  |  |  |  |
|  |  |  |  |

## Analysis and Conclusions

1. We define a "pot" of beans as being the number of beans that has a mass in grams equal to the relative mass of that type of bean. The **Data Table for Part 2** lists the beans by name and symbol, along with their relative masses and the number of beans in a "pot." Examine and compare the numbers of beans in a pot for the various types.

   Allowing for the fact that only whole numbers of beans could be used, and for experimental errors, were the results pretty consistent from type to type? Discuss.

# Report for Experiment 22

**Name**_____

2. Calculate the average number of beans in a pot and express your answer with an uncertainty that reflects the range of variation. As an example, if one were averaging the numbers 26, 28, 29, 29, 28, the average would be reported as $28 \pm 2$; this indicates that none of the numbers being averaged is more than 2 units above or below the average.

3. Calculate the following for each type of bean. Show a sample calculation for one type of bean in each case:

   a. The number of pots in 250 grams.

   b. The number of beans in 250 grams.

   c. The number of pots in 250 beans.

   d. The number of beans in 3.17 pots.

   e. The number of grams in 3.17 pots.

4. You will notice that, in some cases the result is the same no matter which bean is being used, while in other cases, each bean gives a different result. Explain why this must be so.

# Report for Experiment 22     Name_____

5. In Part 2 of the procedure, you were told to determine the number of beans in a pot to the nearest whole number of beans. Similarly, answers to 3(b) and 3(d) should be reported as whole numbers. Why? In what way does this restriction against using a fractional number of beans parallel our understanding of atoms? (**Hint:** Is there such a thing as half an atom?)

6. Explain in a single, well-developed paragraph (grammar and spelling will count), how this experiment simulates the calculation of the relative atomic masses found on the periodic table, and how the "pot" provides an analogy to the mole.

# Report for Experiment 23

## Decomposing Copper Oxide

### Prelaboratory Questions

1. Calculate the percent copper by mass in copper(I) oxide.

2. Calculate the percent copper by mass in copper(II) oxide.

### Data/Observations

1. What is the mass of copper oxide that reacted?

2. What is the mass of copper produced?

### Analysis and Conclusions

1. How could you tell when the reaction was completed?

# Report for Experiment 23

Name_____

**2.** Calculate the percent copper by mass in your copper oxide.

**3.** Compare your result from #2 to the mass percent of copper in copper(I) oxide by finding the difference between the two. Note: you calculated the mass percent of copper in copper(I) oxide in the Prelaboratory Questions.

**4.** Compare your result from #2 to the mass percent of copper in copper(II) oxide by finding the difference between the two. Note: you calculated the mass percent of copper in copper(II) oxide in the Prelaboratory Questions.

**5.** What is the formula of the copper oxide you decomposed? Justify your answer.

**6.** Which would have a larger mass, an iron bar before or after it rusts? Explain your answer.

## Something Extra

Why was the gas sent through the test tube? Could this lab be performed with a test tube open to the air? Explain your answer.

Name_____

Section_____ Date_____

# Report for Experiment 24

## Formula for a Hydrate

### Prelaboratory Questions

**1.** What information is necessary to determine the percentage of water in your hydrate sample?

**2.** How will the water be removed from the hydrate in this experiment?

**3.** A hydrate has the formula of $MgSO_4 \cdot 7H_2O$. What is the percent water in this hydrate?

### Data/Observations

| | |
|---|---|
| Name of salt | |
| Mass of crucible | |
| Mass of crucible + hydrated salt | |
| Mass of hydrated salt | |
| Mass of crucible and contents after heating #1 | |
| Mass of crucible and contents after heating #2 | |
| Mass of crucible and contents after heating #3 | |
| Mass of anhydrous salt | |
| Percentage water in hydrated salt | % water |
| Moles water in hydrated salt | moles |
| Formula for anhydrous salt | |
| Moles anhydrous salt | moles |
| Formula for hydrated salt | |

# Report for Experiment 24     Name_____

## Analysis and Conclusions

1. Determine the percentage of water in the hydrated salt. Think about the fact that the difference between the mass of the hydrated salt and the mass of the anhydrous salt is the mass of the water in the hydrate. Remember the definition of percent.

2. Obtain the name of your anhydrous salt from your teacher. Use it to determine its formula and molar mass.

3. Determine the number of moles of water evaporated from your hydrate. Think about how mass is related to moles.

4. Determine the number of moles of anhydrous salt.

5. Calculate the empirical formula for your hydrated salt. The empirical formula for a hydrate is always written in the form 1 mole anhydrous salt · moles $H_2O$. The 1 mole in front of the anhydrous salt formula is understood and is not written as part of the formula.

6. Why should the crucible and contents be cooled before finding its mass?

# Report for Experiment 24

Name_____

**7.** Why must at least two successive mass readings be equal before finishing the experiment?

**8.** List several possible sources for error in this experiment.

## Something Extra

How could the water be placed back into the crystals? Propose an experiment to test your hypothesis. After checking with your teacher carry out the experiment and report your results.

Name_____

Section_____ Date_____

# Report for Experiment 25

# Recognizing Chemical Reactions

## Prelaboratory Questions

1. What is the distinction between the words "clear" and "colorless" as they apply to solutions? Is a clear solution necessarily colorless? Is a colorless solution necessarily clear? Explain.

2. Explain the difference between chemical changes and physical changes.

3. In complete sentences, define the following terms:
   a. precipitate

   b. reactant

   c. exothermic reaction

# Report for Experiment 25

Name_____

## Data/Observations

### Table 1: The Reactants

| Substance | Physical State | Description |
|-----------|----------------|-------------|
| A | liquid | |
| B | | |
| C | | |
| D | | |
| E | | |

### Table 2: The Reactions

| Substances | Observations (What you saw) | Reaction? (Y/N) | Interpretation (On what did you base your choice?) |
|------------|------------------------------|------------------|----------------------------------------------------|
| A and B | | | |
| A and C | | | |
| A and D | | | |
| A and E | | | |
| B and C | | | |
| B and D | | | |
| B and E | | | |
| C and D | | | |
| C and E | | | |
| D and E | | | |

# Report for Experiment 25

Name_____

## Analysis and Conclusions

1. How did your results compare with those of other groups?  Suggest possible explanations for any significant differences that you observed.

2. If you were to repeat this experiment, how would you change the procedure?  Why would you make that change (or those changes)?

# Report for Experiment 26

## Examples of Chemical Reactions

### Prelaboratory Questions

1. Write and balance chemical equations for the following reactions. Include the state for each substance in the equation.

    **a.** Solid magnesium reacts with aqueous hydrochloric acid to produce aqueous magnesium chloride and hydrogen gas.

    **b.** Aqueous sodium chloride reacts with aqueous silver nitrate to produce solid silver chloride and aqueous sodium nitrate.

    **c.** Solid magnesium burns in the air to form solid magnesium oxide.

### Data/Observations

1. Make a list of observations for Part 1 of the experiment.

# Report for Experiment 26

Name_____

2. Make a list of observations for Part 2 of the experiment.

3. Make a list of observations for Part 3 of the experiment.

4. Make a list of observations for Part 4 of the experiment.

## Analysis and Conclusions

1. For each of the reactions, which observations indicate that a chemical reaction was taking place?

2. What are some clues that accompany chemical changes?

## Something Extra

List three chemical reactions from everyday life that demonstrate the clues that you observed in this lab.

# Report for Experiment 27

## Interpreting Chemical Reactions
### *The Reaction between Copper and Nitric Acid*

## Prelaboratory Questions

1. Use the words, *reactants* and *products* in a sentence which shows that you understand the meanings of the terms.

2. The procedure tells you that a gas will be produced as part of the reaction. Should you expect to see bubbles coming out of the delivery system? Explain.

## Data/Observations

1. Describe the initial appearance of the reactants.

2. Describe all the changes that you observe during the reaction between nitric acid and copper.

# Report for Experiment 27

Name_____

## Analysis and Conclusions

The reactants were copper metal and nitric acid. There were three products formed by the reaction: an aqueous solution of copper(II) nitrate, nitrogen dioxide gas, and water. All five of the participating species are represented below, first in a word equation, then as a molecular equation; neither of the two equations is balanced.

Copper metal + Nitric acid solution → Copper(II) nitrate solution + Nitrogen dioxide gas + Water

$$Cu(s) + HNO_3(aq) \rightarrow Cu(NO_3)_2(aq) + NO_2(g) + H_2O(l)$$

In each of the questions that follow, identify all substances by their name **and** by their symbol or formula, including their physical states: (*s*), (*l*), (*g*), (*aq*). Assume that the water that was part of the nitric acid solution does not take part in the reaction.

1. Which two of the *products* must be in the solution in the test tube? Describe the appearance of each one. What happened to the copper atoms that were originally part of the wire? Where did they go?

2. What is the name and formula of the yellowish gas you saw? What elements are in the yellowish gas? Where did they originate? (From which reactant did they come?)

3. Where did the atoms that formed the water come from (which reactant)?

# Report for Experiment 27    Name_____

**4.** The process that occurred in your test tube was a chemical reaction. Consider how your teacher cleaned the piece of copper wire before the experiment. What happened to the atoms on the surface of the wire? Was this a chemical reaction? Explain.

**5.** The skeleton equation that precedes Question 1 has been copied below. As you see, the same elements are represented on both sides; that is, there are the same kinds of atoms in the reactants as there are in the products: copper, hydrogen, nitrogen, and oxygen. Notice, however, that the *number* of atoms of each element is not the same. Demonstrate the imbalance by completing this atom inventory. Three of the numbers have been supplied to help you get started.

$$Cu(s) + HNO_3(aq) \rightarrow Cu(NO_3)_2(aq) + NO_2(g) + H_2O(l)$$

| **Reactants:** | copper atoms- 1 | **Products:** | copper atoms- |
| | hydrogen atoms- | | hydrogen atoms- |
| | nitrogen atoms- | | nitrogen atoms- |
| | oxygen atoms- 3 | | oxygen atoms- 9 |

**6.** The equation for the reaction between copper metal and nitric acid has been rewritten here, but with one small change: the equation is *balanced*. In other words, not only are the same elements on both sides of the equation, the number of atoms of each element is the same on both sides. Complete this second atom survey, similar to the one in Question 5, to show that the equation is now balanced.

$$Cu(s) + 4 HNO_3(aq) \rightarrow Cu(NO_3)_2(aq) + 2 NO_2(g) + 2 H_2O(l)$$

| **Reactants:** | copper atoms- | **Products:** | copper atoms- |
| | hydrogen atoms- | | hydrogen atoms- |
| | nitrogen atoms- | | nitrogen atoms- |
| | oxygen atoms- | | oxygen atoms- |

# Report for Experiment 27     Name_____

7. One way to define a chemical reaction is to say that it is a process in which the reactant molecules are taken apart, then their atoms are regrouped in a different fashion. Does the reaction between copper and nitric acid fit this definition? Explain.


8. Refer back to your observations. List the ones that demonstrate that a chemical change takes place during this experiment. There are at least four that you should identify. Be specific: don't just say that there was a color change, describe the nature of the change and what it was that underwent the change.


9. During the course of this experiment, the piece of copper wire eventually disappears into the solution. What evidence do you have that this disappearance is more than simply dissolving, such as a sugar cube would do in a glass of water?


10. Look back at your prediction in Prelaboratory Question 2. As it turned out, a gas was formed but there were no bubbles in the beaker of water. How do you explain this?

Name_____

Section_____ Date_____

# Report for Experiment 28

## Conservation of Mass

### Prelaboratory Questions

1. List three examples of situations where mass seems to appear or disappear during a process.

2. What are the reactants in this experiment?

### Data/Observations

|  | Mass of system (g) |
|---|---|
| Empty and unassembled |  |
| Before mixing |  |
| After mixing |  |

|  | Appearance of substances |
|---|---|
| Lead nitrate |  |
| Potassium iodide |  |
| Products after reaction |  |

### Analysis and Conclusions

1. Find the mass of the reactants:  (lead nitrate solution + potassium iodide solution)

2. Find the mass of the products after mixing.

# Report for Experiment 28

**Name**_____

3. How did the masses of the reactants and the products compare?

4. What evidence did you observe that a reaction occurred?

5. Was mass conserved in this reaction? Explain.

6. Was this reaction a physical or chemical change? Explain.

7. What was the reason for stoppering the flask? What do you predict would happen if the experiment was repeated and the chemicals were mixed by simply pouring the test tube contents into the flask?

## Something Extra

For what kind of chemical reaction would it become essential to stopper the flask in order to show conservation of mass?

Name_____

Section_____ Date_____

# Report for Experiment 29

## Reactions in Solution I: Precipitation

### Prelaboratory Questions

1. Write the formulas for the following ionic compounds.
   a. zinc sulfide        b.    chromium(III) hydroxide     c.     lead(II) phosphate

   _____        _____          _____

2. Write chemical equations for the following electrolytes dissolving in water.
   a. sodium chloride

   b. copper(II) chloride

   c. iron(III) sulfate

3. Write a molecular equation for the reaction that occurs when a solution of cobalt(II)nitrate reacts with aqueous potassium phosphate, producing a precipitate of cobalt(II) phosphate and aqueous potassium nitrate.

4. All of the reagent solutions have a concentration of 0.2 $M$. This means that there is 0.2 mole of dissolved substance per liter of solution. What will be the concentration after mixing, assuming you use equal volumes of each solution?

5. How will you recognize formation of a small amount of insoluble solid?

# Report for Experiment 29

Name_____

## Data/Observations

### Data Table

| Group B→ | $CoCl_2$ | $CuCl_2$ | $AlCl_3$ | $BaCl_2$ | $NiCl_2$ |
|---|---|---|---|---|---|
| Group A ↓ | | | | | |
| NaI | | | | | |
| $Na_2CO_3$ | | | | | |
| $Na_3PO_4$ | | | | | |
| $Na_2SO_4$ | | | | | |
| NaOH | | | | | |

## Analysis and Conclusions

For those combinations in which the formation of a precipitate was observed, do each of the following:

**a.** Write the name and formula for the precipitate (remember the principle of electrical neutrality: the total numbers of positive and negative charges must be equal).
**b.** Write a balanced molecular equation for the precipitation reaction that took place.
**c.** Write a balanced ionic equation, showing all dissolved species as ions, and all precipitates as molecules.

There are more than a dozen reactions that occur, so you will need extra space to accomplish your task. The space below is set up for the first two reactions you identify. Attach separate paper for the rest.

**Reaction #1**
**a.** Name and formula of precipitate:

**b.** Molecular equation:

**c.** Ionic equation:

**Reaction #2**
**a.** Name and formula of precipitate:

**b.** Molecular equation:

**c.** Ionic equation:

# Report for Experiment 29

Name_____

## Something Extra

1.  In your ionic equations, you will see that some of the ions in the reactants appear in exactly the same form on the products side of the equation. Ions that are present in a reaction, but which do not take part in the precipitation, are called *spectator ions*. It is sometimes useful to write an abbreviated ionic equation, which can be derived from a complete ionic equation, such as you have written for this experiment. For the reaction between barium chloride and sodium sulfate, the complete ionic equation is:

$$Ba^{2+}(aq) + 2\,Cl^-(aq) + 2\,Na^+(aq) + SO_4{}^{2-}(aq) \rightarrow BaSO_4(s) + 2\,Na^+(aq) + 2\,Cl^-(aq)$$

If we remove the spectators, $Na^+(aq)$ and $Cl^-(aq)$, we have the net ionic equation:

$$Ba^{2+}(aq) + SO_4{}^{2-}(aq) \quad \rightarrow \quad BaSO_4(s)$$

For each of the other precipitates that you found in your experiment, write the net ionic equation for the reaction that took place. As before, attach separate paper to this Report Sheet.

2.  If there were any combinations that appeared to have a reaction, but in which no precipitate was observed, try to identify which ions were responsible for the reaction but do not attempt to write formulas or equations for the reactions. (**Hints:** What ions were present? What possible combinations could account for the reaction? Are there other combinations in the experiment where any of those same ion pairs were present, but reaction did not occur?)

Name_____

Section_____ Date_____

# Report for Experiment 30

## The Activity Series for Metals

### Prelaboratory Questions

1. Identify the following changes as either oxidation or reduction.

   a. $Cu^{2+} \rightarrow Cu$ _____

   b. $Mg \rightarrow Mg^{2+}$ _____

   c. $Fe^{2+} \rightarrow Fe^{3+}$ _____

   d. $2H^+ \rightarrow H_2(g)$ _____

2. Consider the following reaction: $Al(s) + Cr^{3+}(aq) \rightarrow Cr(s) + Al^{3+}(aq)$.

   a. What substance is oxidized? _____

   b. What substance is reduced? _____

3. Aluminum metal will react with a solution of copper(II) ions, but copper metal will not react with a solution of aluminum ions. Which metal is more active, copper or aluminum? ·

   _____

### Data/Observations

1. Reactions

| Cations → <br> Metals ↓ | $Zn^{2+}$ | $Sn^{2+}$ | $Mg^{2+}$ | $Fe^{3+}$ | $Cu^{2+}$ |
|---|---|---|---|---|---|
| Cu | | | | | |
| Fe | | | | | |
| Mg | | | | | |
| Sn | | | | | |
| Zn | | | | | |

2. Observations of reaction between copper and silver nitrate solution.

# Report for Experiment 30

Name_____

## Analysis and Conclusions

1. The metal that reacted with the greatest number of cation solutions is the most active metal you were testing; which one is it?

   _____

2. The metal that reacted with the fewest cation solutions is the least active; which is it?

   _____

3. Rank the remaining three metals, so that you end up with a list of the five metals in order of decreasing activity (most active first). Use the form, (most) > (next) >, etc.

   Most Active                                                                    Least Active

4. Your teacher demonstrated the reaction that occurs when copper metal is placed in a solution of silver ions. Use your observations to place silver in its proper spot on your activity list above.

5. Recalling that the more active metals are those that are more easily oxidized, where on the periodic table would you expect to find the most active metals? Are the more active metals found on the left, the right, or in the middle of the table? What about vertically: are the metals near the top of the table more reactive or less reactive than those toward the bottom?

6. For those cases in which a reaction was observed, write the equation for that reaction. Remember that the number of electrons lost by one kind of atom must equal the number gained by the other, so the total charge on the left side of the arrow must be the same as the total charge on the right side. Add paper, if necessary.

## Something Extra

Consult a table showing the accepted order of metal activities. Your teacher will either suggest a suitable reference or provide you with the list. Discuss your findings on a separate sheet of paper.

# Report for Experiment 31

## Unknown Solutions

### Prelaboratory Questions

1.  Write the formulas for all of the substances in the solutions below the names.

    table sugar                          silver nitrate


    potassium nitrate                    sodium hydroxide


    sulfuric acid                        barium nitrate


    copper (II) nitrate                  ammonium chloride


    sodium chloride                      acetic acid


2.  List methods to test the solutions.
    (**Hint:** Don't forget that you can react the solutions with each other).

    table sugar                          silver nitrate




    potassium nitrate                    sodium hydroxide




    sulfuric acid                        barium nitrate

# Report for Experiment 31     Name_____

copper (II) nitrate              ammonium chloride

sodium chloride                  acetic acid

## Data/Observations

Record all procedures and results of your tests in the table below.

| | Procedures and results |
|---|---|
| Unknown #1 | |
| Unknown #2 | |
| Unknown #3 | |
| Unknown #4 | |
| Unknown #5 | |
| Unknown #6 | |
| Unknown #7 | |
| Unknown #8 | |
| Unknown #9 | |
| Unknown #10 | |

# Report for Experiment 31

Name_____

## Analysis and Conclusions

List each observation and state the possibilities from each observation.

|  | Observations | Possibilities |
|---|---|---|
| Unknown #1 |  |  |
| Unknown #2 |  |  |
| Unknown #3 |  |  |
| Unknown #4 |  |  |
| Unknown #5 |  |  |
| Unknown #6 |  |  |
| Unknown #7 |  |  |
| Unknown #8 |  |  |
| Unknown #9 |  |  |
| Unknown #10 |  |  |

# Report for Experiment 31

**Name**_____

## Summary Table

Fill in the following table:

| | Name | Formula | Reason |
|---|---|---|---|
| Unknown #1 | | | |
| Unknown #2 | | | |
| Unknown #3 | | | |
| Unknown #4 | | | |
| Unknown #5 | | | |
| Unknown #6 | | | |
| Unknown #7 | | | |
| Unknown #8 | | | |
| Unknown #9 | | | |
| Unknown #10 | | | |

## Something Extra

Suppose you were given an unknown solution containing a mixture of two or more of the solutions used in this experiment. Describe what you could do to identify the components of this unknown solution.

# Report for Experiment 32

## Qualitative Analysis:  Anions

### Prelaboratory Questions

1.  Sulfuric acid is used in this experiment.  Describe the process for cleaning up a small amount of sulfuric acid that has spilled on the desktop.

2.  For each of the following, indicate whether there is evidence of a chemical change.
    a.  Mixing two clear, colorless solutions causes formation of a bright yellow solid.

    b.  Mixing two clear, colorless solutions produces some bubbles which eventually disappear, leaving a clear, colorless solution.

    c.  Mixing two clear, colorless solutions initially gives a clear, colorless solution.  As it stands, the solution turns hazy.

    d.  Addition of a white solid to a clear, colorless solution produces some bubbles that disappear after about 5-10 seconds, leaving a clear, colorless solution.

### Data/Observations
### Part 1

| Anion | Result with $Fe^{2+}$ | Effect of $H_2SO_4$ | Result with $Fe^{3+}$ | Effect of $H_2SO_4$ |
|---|---|---|---|---|
| bromide | | | | |
| chloride | | | | |
| iodide | | | | |
| carbonate | | | | |
| sulfate | | | | |
| phosphate | | | | |
| oxalate | | | | |
| nitrate | | | | |
| hydroxide | | | | |
| thiosulfate | | | | |

Name_____

## Part 2

| Anion | Result with Ag⁺ |
|---|---|
| bromide | |
| chloride | |
| iodide | |
| carbonate | |
| sulfate | |
| phosphate | |
| oxalate | |
| nitrate | |
| hydroxide | |
| thiosulfate | |

## Part 3

For each unknown, briefly describe what you did, what you observed and what information you got from that test. Remember that "no reaction" can be just as useful as appearance of a precipitate, if it allows you to eliminate some possibilities.

**Unknown #1**

**Unknown #2**

**Unknown #3**

# Report for Experiment 32

**Name**_____

## Analysis and Conclusions

1. Suppose you were given three unlabeled solutions. You know that one contains iron(II), another contains iron(III) and the third has silver ion, but you don't know which is which. Devise a scheme by which you could identify each of the three cation solutions.

2. Explain how you can distinguish among solutions containing bromide, chloride and iodide ions.

3. Explain how you can determine whether oxalate ion is present in a solution.

Name_____

Section_____ Date_____

# Report for Experiment 33

## The Halide Family

### Prelaboratory Questions

1. What is a *precipitate*?

2. At one point in the procedure, you will try two different tests on the same precipitate. Describe the process for dividing the precipitate into two separate samples.

3. Write equations for each of the following processes.
   a. Sodium thiosulfate dissolves in water.

   b. A precipitate forms when solutions of silver nitrate and sodium iodide are mixed.

### Data/Observations

#### Summary Table

| Anion | Reaction with $Ca^{2+}$ | Reaction with $Ag^+$ | Response to starch | Response to bleach |
|---|---|---|---|---|
| Fluoride, $F^-$ | | | | |
| Chloride, $Cl^-$ | | | | |
| Bromide, $Br^-$ | | | | |
| Iodide, $I^-$ | | | | |

# Report for Experiment 33

Name_____

## Part 2

Effect of ammonia, $NH_3$, and thiosulfate ion, $S_2O_3^{2-}$, on precipitates

with $NH_3$: AgCl

AgBr

AgI

with $S_2O_3^{2-}$: AgCl

AgBr

AgI

## Part 4 (If done)

Describe the effect of adding hexane to each of the tubes.

Describe the colors of each of the two layers after mixing with chlorine water, $Cl_2(aq)$

fluoride, $F^-$:          top

bottom

bromide, $Br^-$:          top

bottom

chloride, $Cl^-$:          top

bottom

iodide, $I^-$:          top

bottom

## Part 5 Unknowns

For each of your unknowns, indicate the tests that allowed you to identify the ion or ions present. Include what reagents you used in the tests and what you observed.

**First Unknown**          Number on tube

Evidence:

Ion present

# Report for Experiment 33

**Name**_____

**Second Unknown**     Number on tube               Ions present
                       Evidence:

## Analysis and Conclusions

1. Explain what information you found from each of the first three (or four) parts of this experiment. Make separate clear, concise and grammatically correct statements for each part. Someone else should be able to use your results to analyze the unknowns successfully.

2. In what way does fluoride ion behave differently from the other three ions in the family?

3. In what way(s) do chloride, bromide, and iodide ions behave similarly? In what way(s) do they display different chemical behavior?

# Report for Experiment 33          Name_____

4. How can you distinguish between:
   a. chloride ion and bromide ion?




   b. chloride ion and iodide ion?




   c. bromide ion and iodide ion?




## Something Extra

1. If you did the optional tests from Part 4, describe and account for the color changes you observed during Cleaning Up.




2. A common test for the presence of starch is formation of a dark, blue-black color when iodine, $I_2$, is added. How do you account for the color you observed in Part 3? What must have happened?

# Report for Experiment 34

## Copper Wire
## in a Solution of Silver Nitrate

### Prelaboratory Questions

1. Write the unbalanced equation for the reaction between copper and silver nitrate.

2. How many atoms are there in a 10.4 gram sample of copper?

3. How many $AgNO_3$ units are there in a 2.2 gram sample of silver nitrate?

4. In another experiment 1.65 g of lead nitrate, $Pb(NO_3)_2$, react with 0.327 g zinc, Zn. What is the mole relationship between the lead nitrate and the zinc?

### Data/Observations

mass of copper wire before reaction _____ g

mass of vial and silver nitrate _____ g

mass of empty vial _____ g

mass of empty 150-mL beaker _____ g

mass of copper wire after reaction _____ g

mass of beaker with dried residue _____ g

# Report for Experiment 34

**Name**_____

## Analysis and Conclusions

1. Calculate the change in the mass of the copper wire.

2. Calculate the mass of silver nitrate used.

3. Calculate the mass of residue (silver) obtained.

4. Determine the number of moles of copper that reacted.

5. Determine the number of moles of silver nitrate used in the reaction.

6. Determine the number of moles of silver produced in the reaction.

7. From your data, determine the ratio:     $\dfrac{\text{moles Ag}}{\text{moles Cu}}$

   Express your answer as a decimal to the proper number of significant digits.

# Report for Experiment 34

Name_____

8. From your data, determine the ratio:  $\dfrac{\text{moles Ag}}{\text{moles AgNO}_3}$

9. Summarize your results below:

| Substance | Mass | Moles |
|---|---|---|
| AgNO$_3$ used | | |
| Cu wire used | | |
| Ag produced | | |

10. Write a balanced chemical equation for the reaction between copper and silver nitrate.

11. How many atoms of copper reacted in this experiment? How many atoms of silver were produced?

12. How do the ratios that you calculated in 7 and 8 above relate to the balanced equation?

# Report for Experiment 34

**13.** What caused the color that you observed in the 150-mL beaker as the experiment proceeded?

**14.** Why was the mass that the copper lost not equal to the mass of the silver that formed?

## Something Extra

**1.** The values obtained by the class for the Ag:Cu ratio and for the Ag:AgNO$_3$ ratio will be listed on the board. Use the posted information to calculate the average ratios for the class.

**a.** How do you explain a Ag:Cu ratio which is higher than the average? Lower than the average?

**b.** How do you explain a Ag:AgNO$_3$ ratio which is higher than the average? Lower than the average?

# Report for Experiment 35

# Mass Relationships In Chemical Compounds

## Prelaboratory Questions

1. Of the types of reactions discussed in Chapters 7 and 8 of your text, which type would most likely begin with a single reactant and involve an apparent decrease in mass.

2. Why must you avoid using the stirring rod to break up the solid while it is in the filter?

3. Discuss the effects that might result from the following typical student technique errors. Specify whether the mass of the sample will appear to be greater or less than it should be.
   a. The student forgets to find the mass of the empty beaker before beginning, and uses the mass of another beaker in the calculations.

   b. The student finds the mass of the empty beaker, then adds a masking-tape label for ease of identification later.

   c. The student uses a stirring rod to break up the product, then places the rod on the desk top between uses.

   d. To save time, the student finds the mass of the filter paper and product immediately after filtration, rather than waiting for it to dry overnight.

# Report for Experiment 35

Name_____

## Data/Observations

| | |
|---|---|
| mass of labeled beaker | _____ g |
| mass of beaker and unknown sample | _____ g |
| mass of beaker and sample after heating | _____ g |
| mass of filter paper | _____ g |
| mass of filter and dried product | _____ g |

1. Describe the changes that occurred:

   **a.** during heating of the blue solid

   **b.** as the first few drops of water were added to the brown solid

   **c.** when aluminum was added to the blue solution

2. Describe the appearance of the contents of the beaker at the start of Day 2.

## Analysis and Conclusions

1. Calculate the mass of the original sample, the mass lost during heating and the mass of solid remaining in the beaker.

   mass of original sample: _____ g

   mass lost during heating: _____ g

   mass of solid after heating: _____ g

# Report for Experiment 35

Name_____

2.  Calculate the mass of final product.

mass of final product: _____ g

3.  Calculate the ratio of the mass of final product to the mass of the original blue solid.

$$\frac{\text{mass of final product}}{\text{mass of original sample}} =$$

4.  Calculate the ratio of the mass of final product to the mass of the solid remaining after heating.

$$\frac{\text{mass of final product}}{\text{mass of solid after heating}} =$$

5.  Given what you observed when you added distilled water in step 4, suggest a reasonable explanation for the mass loss during heating.

6.  What might have happened if you had left the beaker and contents from step 3 overnight before finding the mass.

7.  Cite at least three examples of evidence for chemical change that you observed in step 5. Of the categories of reactions discussed in your text, which type was involved in step 5 of the procedure?  How do you know?

8.  Does your final product appear to be the same substance as either of the other solids in this experiment?      (Don't include aluminum in your consideration.)  Explain.

# Report for Experiment 35

Name_____

9. Compare your ratios from calculations 3 and 4 to those of other teams. Are the results consistent or do they appear to vary in a random fashion? Does this experiment illustrate the Law of Constant Composition? Explain.

10. In view of your answers to Questions 5-7, and given the demonstration your teacher carried out during the post-laboratory discussion, did the heating of the original blue solid result in a chemical change or a physical change. Explain.

## Something Extra

Now that you have analyzed the mass ratios involved, it is time to see how well your data extend to include mole ratios. Here is an overview of what has happened in this experiment.

$$CuCl_2 \cdot 2H_2O(s) \xrightarrow{\Delta} CuCl_2(s) + 2H_2O(g)$$

The initial heating of the blue solid simply removed water from a sample of hydrated copper(II) chloride. Many compounds absorb water from the air into their crystalline structure.
Here is the equation for the dehydration:

The $\Delta$ above the arrow indicates heat is necessary for the process. Once the brown solid was cooled and weighed, you slowly added water to it. At first, the water simply replaced what had been lost during heating, but as you added more and more water, you dissolved the copper(II) chloride, forming a solution. Addition of aluminum resulted in a single replacement reaction:

$$2Al(s) + 3CuCl_2(aq) \longrightarrow 3Cu(s) + 2AlCl_3(aq)$$

Answer the following, showing your calculations in the space provided.

1. The last product you obtained (in the filter paper) was copper metal (step 10).
   a. What mass of copper did you recover?

   _____ g

   b. How many moles of copper did you recover?

   _____ mol

# Report for Experiment 35

Name_____

c.  How many moles of aluminum must have reacted?

_____ mol

d.  What mass of aluminum was consumed?

_____ g

2.  The light brown solid that was left after the heating consisted only of copper and chlorine. Assume that the mass of the copper that you recovered in step 10 was the same as the mass of copper present in the compound of copper and chlorine remaining after step 3.

a.  What mass of chlorine was in the compound?

_____ g

b.  How many moles of chlorine were in the compound?

_____ mol

c.  What was the mole ratio of chlorine to copper in the compound?

_____ mol Cl/mol Cu

3.  The ratio you reported in 2c, above, represents the number of chlorine atoms per copper atom in the compound, so it must be a whole number ratio (1/1, 2/1, 3/2, 3/1, etc.)

a.  What whole-number ratio best matches your answer to 2c?

b.  Write the formula for the compound.

4.  Copper only forms two cations, $Cu^+$ and $Cu^{2+}$; chloride is always $Cl^-$. Based on your experimental results, did you have a sample of CuCl or of $CuCl_2$? Defend your choice.

# Report for Experiment 35

**Name**_____

**5.** Starting with the mass of the copper chloride you had in the beaker after step 3, calculate:

   **a.** the number of moles of copper chloride.

_____ mol

   **b.** the number of moles and the mass of copper that should be present in your sample of copper chloride. This is your theoretical yield.

_____ mol

_____ g

   **c.** Divide the mass of copper actually recovered (step 10) by the theoretical yield you just calculated, then multiply that answer by 100%. This is your percent yield.

_____ %

**6.** The initial heating drove off water that had been trapped in the copper chloride sample.

   **a.** What mass of water was driven off during heating?

_____ g

   **b.** How many moles of water were driven off?

_____ mol

   **c.** In the original blue-green compound, what is the mole ratio of:
     **i.** water to copper        **ii.** water to chlorine

# Report for Experiment 36

## The Calcium Content of Milk

### Prelaboratory Questions

**1.** Why would you expect the calcium in milk to be present as calcium ions, rather than as elemental calcium?

**2.** According to one source, one cup (~240 mL) of whole milk contains 291 mg of calcium. Use this to calculate the mass percent of calcium in whole milk. Assume the density of milk is 1.0 g/mL.

**3.** Would you expect the density of milk to be affected by its fat content? Explain. Would increased fat content raise or lower the density? Explain.

### Data/Observations

**Data Table**

**Titration 1:**

| | | | | |
|---|---|---|---|---|
| Initial mass of milk pipet | g | Initial mass of EDTA pipet | | g |
| Final mass of milk pipet | g | Final mass of EDTA pipet | | g |
| Mass of milk used | g | Mass of EDTA used | | g |

**Titration 2:**

| | | | | |
|---|---|---|---|---|
| Initial mass of milk pipet | g | Initial mass of EDTA pipet | | g |
| Final mass of milk pipet | g | Final mass of EDTA pipet | | g |
| Mass of milk used | g | Mass of EDTA used | | g |

# Report for Experiment 36    Name_____

## Titration 3:

| | | | |
|---|---|---|---|
| Initial mass of milk pipet | g | Initial mass of EDTA pipet | g |
| Final mass of milk pipet | g | Final mass of EDTA pipet | g |
| Mass of milk used | g | Mass of EDTA used | g |

## Analysis and Conclusions

1.  The concentration of the EDTA solution has been adjusted so that exactly 1 gram of EDTA solution will tie up exactly 1.08 mg of calcium. Calculate the number of milligrams of calcium present in each of your three titration samples. Show your work for the first titration below. You need report only the results of the other two.

    If you carried out more than three titrations, base all your calculations on the three that show the best agreement.

    mg $Ca^{2+}$ present: Trial 1 _____mg

    mg $Ca^{2+}$ present: Trial 2 _____mg

    mg $Ca^{2+}$ present: Trial 3 _____mg

2.  Use your results from the first calculation to determine the number of milligrams of calcium in 1 cup (~240 mL) of milk. Report both the individual values for the three samples and an average value. Assume that skim milk has the same density as water. Show your work for trial 1 below.

    mg $Ca^{2+}$ per cup: Trial 1 _____mg

    mg $Ca^{2+}$ per cup: Trial 2 _____mg

    mg $Ca^{2+}$ per cup: Trial 3 _____mg

    mg $Ca^{2+}$ per cup: (Average) _____mg

3.  Calculate the individual deviations from the average for each trial. Calculate the average deviation for your three trials.

    Trial 1 deviation: _____ mg

    Trial 2 deviation: _____ mg

    Trial 3 deviation: _____ mg

    Average deviation: _____ mg

# Report for Experiment 36

Name_____

4. When an average deviation is known for a series of analyses, the results of the analysis are generally given in the form: (average value) ± (average deviation). Report the concentration of calcium in milk with the average deviation as follows:

Concentration of $Ca^{2+}$ = _____mg ± _____mg/cup

5. Calculate the percent deviation for your experimental results. Show your work below.

_____ %

6. The USRDA for calcium is 1200 mg per day. What fraction of the daily requirement would one cup of milk provide based on your average value?

7. According to the carton label, one cup of milk provides 35% of the USRDA for calcium. What is your percentage error, assuming the carton value is correct?

8. Women over the age of 50 and men over age of 65 need about 50% more calcium than younger adults. Why is this?

# Report for Experiment 36

Name_____

9. A student purchased a calcium supplement tablet which contained calcium carbonate. The student placed the tablet in water for several hours. Addition of NaOH and the indicator gave a blue solution. What does this indicate? Does this test show that the supplement is not giving the student any useful calcium? Explain your reasoning. (**Hint:** Consider solubility rules.)

## Something Extra

**Suggestions for further investigation:** These are optional, but be aware that it will be up to you, not the teacher, to provide the materials for options 1 and 3

1. Repeat the experiment, but use powdered milk (reconstituted with water).

2. Try the experiment on a larger scale. Try 5.0-mL samples of milk, using small glass vessels (such as 10-mL Erlenmeyer flasks or 20-mL beakers) in place of the 24-well test plate. Calculate the quantities of other reagents you expect to need and show your calculations to your teacher before you begin this extension.

3. Use a calcium supplement tablet. Consult your teacher; it may be necessary to use acetic acid or some other dilute acid to dissolve the calcium tablet. (This is a hint for Question 9, above.)

Name_____

Section_____ Date_____

# Report for Experiment 37

# Stoichiometry

## Prelaboratory Questions

1.  Write out and balance each of the following equations.

copper(II) sulfate(*aq*) + iron(*s*) → copper(*s*) + iron(II) sulfate(*aq*)

copper(II) sulfate(*aq*) + iron(*s*) → copper(*s*) + iron(III) sulfate(*aq*)

2.  If iron(III) sulfate were formed, what mass of copper would be expected?

3.  If iron(II) sulfate were formed, what mass of copper would be expected?

# Report for Experiment 37

Name_____

## Data/Observations

1.  Table 7.1 lists clues that a chemical reaction has occurred. Which of the observations you made support that a chemical reaction has occurred in the experiment?

2.  What mass of copper was formed?

## Analysis and Conclusions

1.  Which reactant was limiting? What observations support this? Also, use the chemical equation for the reaction that occurred in this lab and stoichiometric calculations to support your answer.

2.  Why were the amounts chosen so this reactant (see number 1 above) was limiting? What would be a problem with having the other reactant as the limiting reactant?

# Report for Experiment 37

**Name**_____

3. Why was the copper washed with water (step 9 of the procedure)?

4. Why didn't the water added to the copper(II) sulfate have to be measured exactly?

5. What is the formula for the iron-containing compound that is formed when copper(II) sulfate and iron react? Support your answer.

## Something Extra

Remove the copper metal and let the solution stand for a few days. What happens? Explain.

# Report for Experiment 38

## Calorimetry and Limiting Reactants

### Prelaboratory Questions

1. Determine the number of moles of acid and base for each trial and record your results in the Summary Tables. Show a sample calculation in the space below.

2. If two separate 50.0 mL samples of the NaOH are mixed with 25.0 mL portions of HCl and $H_2SO_4$, respectively, which combination should produce the greater quantity of heat energy? Why?

### Data/Observations

| Combination tested | Initial Temperature | Final Temperature | ΔT |
|---|---|---|---|
| 20.0 mL NaOH + 5.0 mL Acid A | | | |
| 20.0 mL NaOH + 10.0 mL Acid A | | | |
| 20.0 mL NaOH + 15.0 mL Acid A | | | |
| 20.0 mL NaOH + 20.0 mL Acid A | | | |
| 20.0 mL NaOH + 25.0 mL Acid A | | | |
| 20.0 mL NaOH + 5.0 mL Acid B | | | |
| 20.0 mL NaOH + 10.0 mL Acid B | | | |
| 20.0 mL NaOH + 15.0 mL Acid B | | | |
| 20.0 mL NaOH + 20.0 mL Acid B | | | |
| 20.0 mL NaOH + 25.0 mL Acid B | | | |

# Report for Experiment 38

Name_____

## Analysis and Conclusions

1. Compare the temperature changes. Which combination produced the greatest change in temperature? Was your acid hydrochloric acid or sulfuric acid? Cite experimental evidence to support your choice.

2. In all but one of the trials there was a limiting reactant.
   a. Based on your answer to question 1, which cases involved a limiting reactant? Identify which reactant (acid or NaOH) was limiting and cite experimental evidence or mathematical proof for each case in which there was a limiting reactant.

   b. In which trial was there not a limiting reactant? Defend your choice.

3. Construct a graph of temperature change versus volume of acid added for your acid. On the same set of axes, but in a different color, sketch the graph you would *expect to get* if you were to use the other acid. Explain your reasoning.

4. When you did each trial, the calculator screen showed you a plot of temperature as a function of time. Sketch the shape of one of those graphs and account for what you see. Indicate on your sketch the initial and final temperatures.

# Report for Experiment 38

**Name**_____

## Summary Tables

| Volume acid A | Volume NaOH | Moles acid A | Moles NaOH | Which is limiting? | Temperature change |
|---|---|---|---|---|---|
| 5.00 mL | 20.0 mL | | | | |
| 10.0 mL | 20.0 mL | | | | |
| 15.0 mL | 20.0 mL | | | | |
| 20.0 mL | 20.0 mL | | | | |
| 25.0 mL | 20.0 mL | | | | |

| Volume acid B | Volume NaOH | Moles acid B | Moles NaOH | Which is limiting? | Temperature change |
|---|---|---|---|---|---|
| 5.00 mL | 20.0 mL | | | | |
| 10.0 mL | 20.0 mL | | | | |
| 15.0 mL | 20.0 mL | | | | |
| 20.0 mL | 20.0 mL | | | | |
| 25.0 mL | 20.0 mL | | | | |

## Something Extra

1. Is the heat that is produced in the reaction between an acid and a base dependent on the strength of the acid or base? To answer this question measure the heat produced by the following combinations of acids and bases:
   a. Strong acid-strong base: HCl and NaOH.
   b. Strong acid-weak base: HCl and $NH_3(aq)$.
   c. Weak acid-strong base: $HC_2H_3O_2$ and NaOH.
   d. Weak acid-weak base: $HC_2H_3O_2$ and $NH_3$.

   Use 20.0 mL of each reactant.

   **Note:** Ammonia has a strong, unpleasant odor. Do these experiments in a fume hood or in a well-ventilated room.

2. Use a computer program such as Logger Pro™ to plot the results of each reaction. Compare the plots in terms of $\Delta T$ values and the time needed to reach the maximum temperature in each case. Account for any differences you find.

Name_____

Section_____ Date_____

# Report for Experiment 39

## Synthesis of Manganese(II) Chloride

### Prelaboratory Questions

1.  Explain the difference between *theoretical yield* and *actual yield*.


2.  Why is it important for the manganese to react entirely before proceeding at step 5?



3.  What is a desiccator, and why is it needed in this experiment?



4.  a.  If 10 *M* HCl(aq) accidentally spills or splashes on your skin or clothing, describe in detail what you should do.


    b.  What, if anything, would you do differently if the acid spilled on the surface of the lab bench or hood?



5.  When you are done with the manganese(II) chloride, how should you dispose of the product?


## Data/Observations

Mass of empty Erlenmeyer flask (with boiling stone):     _____ g

Mass of Erlenmeyer flask and manganese metal:     _____ g

Mass of flask and manganese(II) chloride:     _____ g

Final mass of flask and manganese(II) chloride:     _____ g

Appearance of manganese(II) chloride:

# Report for Experiment 39

Name_____

Was the reaction between manganese metal and hydrochloric acid endothermic or exothermic? Describe the evidence on which you base your answer.

## Analysis and Conclusions
**Show all work.**

1. Calculate the mass and the number of moles of manganese metal used.

2. Use the final mass of the flask and product to find the mass and number of moles of manganese(II) chloride produced. This is your actual yield.

3. Calculate the mass of manganese(II) chloride you would expect to produce from the original mass of manganese metal. This is your theoretical yield.

4. Determine the percent yield of manganese(II) chloride.

$$100\% = \frac{\text{Actual Yield}}{\text{Theoretical Yield}} = \text{Percent Yield}$$

# Report for Experiment 39

Name_____

5. Predict the effect on your yield of these procedural errors. In each case, will the reported mass of manganese(II) chloride be too high or too low? Give a reason for each answer.

    a. The manganese metal used was impure; it had a coating of manganese oxide.

    b. Some of the solution was lost during evaporation because of spattering.

    c. The water was not completely evaporated.

    d. During cooling, the flask was left in the open air instead of in a desiccator.

6. Was your percent yield greater than or less than 100%? Suggest possible explanations for any significant variation (greater than about 5%) from 100% yield. You are not limited to the choices given in question 5. Base your answer on your own experience doing the experiment.

7. Explain how you arrived at the number of significant figures you show for your percent yield.

# Report for Experiment 40

## Energy Value of Nuts

### Prelaboratory Questions

1. Paraffin wax has the chemical formula $C_{25}H_{52}$. Write a balanced equation for the combustion of paraffin in air.

2. How much energy is required to warm 100 g of $H_2O$ from 20°C to 80°C if it is initially in a 140 g glass flask? (The specific heat of water is 4.18 J/g °C; the specific heat of glass is 0.836 J/g °C.).

3. Predict which of these three nuts: peanuts, cashews, or almonds, will furnish the greatest amount of energy per gram. Explain briefly your hypothesis.

# Report for Experiment 40

Name_____

## Data/Observations

|  | Sample 1 | Sample 2 | Sample 3 |
|---|---|---|---|
| mass of nut$_{initial}$ |  |  |  |
| mass of beaker |  |  |  |
| volume of water |  |  |  |
| T$_{initial}$ of water |  |  |  |
| T$_{final}$ of water |  |  |  |
| mass of remnant |  |  |  |

## Analysis and Conclusions

Show a sample calculation for each of the questions 1-5, and then record your results in the Summary Table.

1. Determine the change in mass of the nut as a result of combustion.

2. Determine the change in temperature of the water and beaker as a result of combustion of the nut.

3. Determine the heat absorbed by the water, using the equation $\Delta H = s \times m \times \Delta T$. (The specific heat, $s$, for water is 4.18 J/g $^\circ$C).

4. Determine the heat absorbed by the beaker. (The specific heat for glass is 0.836 J/g $^\circ$C).

# Report for Experiment 40

Name_____

**5.** Determine the total heat absorbed by the water and the beaker. **Note:** This heat is equal to the heat released by the nut.

**6.** Determine the total heat released per gram of nut.

## Summary Table

|  | Sample 1 | Sample 2 | Sample 3 |
|---|---|---|---|
| Mass of combusted nut |  |  |  |
| Change in T ($\Delta T$) |  |  |  |
| Heat absorbed by the water |  |  |  |
| Heat absorbed by the beaker |  |  |  |
| Total heat absorbed |  |  |  |
| Total heat released per gram of nut |  |  |  |

## Something Extra

**1.** A serving size of nuts or chips is often listed on food packages as 1 ounce (28.35 g). Using your lab data, determine the energy value per serving for each of the nut samples you used.

# Report for Experiment 40

Name_____

2. Critique the procedure used in this experiment. Do you expect the procedure to give an accurate energy value for the nuts? Explain your answer.

3. Compare your results to the nutritional information listed on the packages of commercially available products.

Name_____

Section_____ Date_____

# Report for Experiment 41

## Specific Heat of a Metal

## Prelaboratory Questions

1. Since the specific heat of water is given in units of joules per *gram* degree Celsius why do we measure the volume of water in the calorimeter instead of its mass?

2. A 22.50-g piece of an unknown metal is heated to 100.°C then transferred quickly and without cooling into 100. mL of water at 20.0°C. The final temperature reached by the system is 26.9°C.
   a. Calculate the quantity of heat absorbed by the water. Show all work.

   b. Determine the quantity of heat lost by the piece of metal. Show all work.

   c. Calculate the specific heat of the metal in J/g °C. Show all work.

3. What would be the effect on the value of the specific heat capacity of water if all temperatures were measured in kelvins (K) rather than degrees Celsius (°C)? Explain.

# Report for Experiment 41

**Name**_____

## Data/Observations Spaces are provided for three trials.

| | | | |
|---|---|---|---|
| Volume of water used | _____ mL | _____ mL | _____ mL |
| Mass of water used | _____ g | _____ g | _____ g |
| Initial temperature of water | _____ °C | _____ °C | _____ °C |
| Final temperature of water | _____ °C | _____ °C | _____ °C |
| Temperature difference for water | _____ °C | _____ °C | _____ °C |
| Mass and identity of metal sample | _____ g | _____ g | _____ g |

_____
(Name of metal)

| | | | |
|---|---|---|---|
| Initial temperature of metal | _____ °C | _____ °C | _____ °C |
| Final temperature of metal | _____ °C | _____ °C | _____ °C |
| Temperature difference for metal | _____ °C | _____ °C | _____ °C |

## Analysis and Conclusions

1. Calculate the quantity of heat gained by the water, using Equation 1. If you carried out additional trials, report the results of all trials, as well as an average (mean) value. You need to show your work for only one of the trials.

$q = $ _____ J

$q = $ _____ J

$q = $ _____ J

(mean) $q = $ _____ J

# Report for Experiment 41

**Name**_____

2. Assume that the quantity of heat lost by the metal is equal to the quantity of heat gained by the water. Use Equation 1 to determine the specific heat, **s**, of the metal. Be sure you use $\Delta T$ for the metal in your calculation. As before, if you carried out multiple trials, report the result for each, as well as a mean value. Show the calculations for the first trial only.

| | | |
|---|---|---|
| s = | _____ | J/g•°C |
| s = | _____ | J/g•°C |
| s = | _____ | J/g•°C |
| (mean) s = | _____ | J/g•°C |

3. Consider the assumption you were asked to make in the previous calculation (#2).
   a. Explain why the assumption is not valid.

   b. Does using the assumption from #2 give a value for the specific heat of the metal that is too high or too low? Explain.

4. Look up the value of the specific heat of your metal in the *Handbook of Chemistry and Physics*. Calculate your percent error, using the following equation (note the "absolute value" signs).

$$\% \text{ error} = \frac{|(\text{accepted value}) - (\text{experimental value})|}{(\text{accepted value})} \times 100\%$$

# Report for Experiment 41

**Name**_____

## Something Extra

1. Any calorimeter absorbs a certain amount of the heat released. Knowing this, is your value of the specific heat of the metal more likely to be higher or lower than the accepted value? Explain.

2. Develop a procedure for determining the heat capacity of the calorimeter that you used. With your teacher's approval, carry out your procedure.

# Report for Experiment 42

# Which is Your Metal?

## Prelaboratory Questions

1. How do you know the final temperature of the metal?

2. Why do you use a hot water bath to heat the metal?

3. Why do you measure the volume of the water in the calorimeter when we need to know the mass of the water for the calculations?

## Data/Observations

Fill in the following table:

|  | Trial #1 | Trial #2 | Trial #3 |
|---|---|---|---|
| Mass of metal |  |  |  |
| Mass of water (calorimeter) |  |  |  |
| Initial temp. of metal |  |  |  |
| Initial temp. of water |  |  |  |
| Final temp. of water |  |  |  |

# Report for Experiment 42

**Name_____**

## Analysis and Conclusions

1. Calculate the heat transferred to the water in the calorimeter in each trial.

    Trial #1:



    Trial #2:



    Trial #3:



2. How does the heat transferred to the water in the calorimeter compare to the heat transferred from the metal in the calorimeter?



3. Calculate the specific heat capacity of your metal in each trial.

    Trial #1:



    Trial #2:



    Trial #3:

# Report for Experiment 42

**Name**_____

4. Calculate the average specific heat capacity of your metal.

5. What is the identity of your metal?

6. Assuming the identity of your metal is correct, what is your percent error in the specific heat capacity?

7. Both of the following errors would cause a change in the calculated specific heat capacity for your metal. Tell if the change would be to raise or lower your calculated value of the specific heat capacity. Explain.
   a. A significant amount of water is transferred with the hot metal.

   b. The metal "cools off" as you transfer it from the hot water to the calorimeter.

# Report for Experiment 42     Name_____

8. Suppose that in the procedure you added metal at room temperature to hot water. How do you think this would affect your percent error (higher, lower, or the same)? Explain your reasoning.

## Something Extra
Will you get similar results if you use a beaker instead of nested foam cups? What about a paper cup? Try it.

# Report for Experiment 43

## Stoichiometry and Calorimetry

### Prelaboratory Questions

1. Hypochlorite is an oxidizing reagent. In this reaction the sulfite is oxidized to sulfate and the chlorine atom in the $OCl^-$ ion will either become molecular chlorine or chloride ion.

   a. In addition to the method used in this experiment, how else could you decide whether the chlorine atom in hypochlorite becomes chloride ion or molecular chlorine?

   b. Write balanced molecular equations for the formation of each of the two possible chlorine products. Remember these are alkaline solutions, so water and hydroxide ions (from sodium hydroxide) may also be involved.

   c. How will you decide which of the two equations correctly represents the reaction between sulfite and hypochlorite?

# Report for Experiment 43

Name_____

## Data/Observations

| Trial | Mol OCl⁻/mol SO₃²⁻ | Initial Temperature | Final Temperature |
|-------|--------------------|--------------------|-------------------|
| 1 | 3:1 | | |
| 2 | 2:1 | | |
| 3 | 3:2 (or 1.5:1) | | |
| 4 | 1:1 | | |
| 5 | 2:3 (or 1:1.5) | | |
| 6 | 1:2 | | |
| 7 | 1:3 | | |

## Analysis and Conclusions

### Summary Table

| Trial | Mol OCl⁻/mol SO₃²⁻ | q (J) | ΔH (kJ/mol NaOCl) |
|-------|--------------------|-------|---------------------|
| 1 | 3:1 | | |
| 2 | 2:1 | | |
| 3 | 3:2 (or 1.5:1) | | |
| 4 | 1:1 | | |
| 5 | 2:3 (or 1:1.5) | | |
| 6 | 1:2 | | |
| 7 | 1:3 | | |

1. For each trial calculate $q$, the quantity of heat released by the reaction and enter your result in the Summary Table. Assume that each of the solution combinations has the same specific heat as water, 4.184 J/g°C. Note also that the total mass of solution being heated is 24.0 g in each case. Show the calculation for Trial 1 below.

# Report for Experiment 43

Name_____

2. To determine the stoichiometry of this reaction we need to establish the mole ratio that produces the maximum amount of heat.

   a. Use the volume and concentration of sodium hypochlorite to calculate the number of moles of sulfite ion present in each reaction system. Show your work for Trial 1.

   b. Use the numbers of moles just calculated and the value of $q$ for each reaction (from **question 1** to calculate values of $\Delta H$ for each reaction in kJ/mol NaOCl. Show the calculation for Trial 1 and record the values for all of the trials in the Summary Table.

3. Based on your answer to **question 2b**, which combination produced the greatest amount of heat per mole of sodium hypochlorite consumed? This must be the reaction combination that is closest to the actual stoichiometry of the reaction. Choose the equation from the Prelaboratory Question that matches the mole ratio of sodium hypochlorite to sodium sulfite for your experimental result.

# Report for Experiment 43     Name_____

## Something Extra

1. You were told to base your decision on the number of moles of sodium hypochlorite consumed. That was an arbitrary choice. Do the calculations necessary to show that the same results would be obtained and the same decision would have been made had you based your calculations in **2b** on the moles of sodium sulfite consumed, instead of on moles of sodium hypochlorite.

2. Repeat the experiment, using the same concentrations and volume combinations, but replace the sodium sulfite with either:
   **a.** sodium thiosulfate, $Na_2S_2O_3$, or
   **b.** sodium iodide. Follow the instructions for the original experiment.

# Report for Experiment 44

## Heat of Reaction

### Prelaboratory Questions

1. Write net ionic equations for the three processes in this experiment.

2. Use Hess's Law to find the heat of reaction for: C(graphite) → C(diamond) given the following information:

$$C(graphite) + O_2(g) → CO_2(g) \qquad \Delta H = -393.7 \text{ kJ/mol}$$
$$C(diamond) + O_2(g) → CO_2(g) \qquad \Delta H = -392.2 \text{ kJ/mol}$$

3. For any given chemical reaction, how does the heat of the reaction depend on the mass of substance used in the reaction.

4. How many Joules are required to warm 250 mL of water from 20.5°C to 43.7°C?

# Report for Experiment 44

**Name**_____

## Data/Observations

### Data Table 1

|  | Reaction 1 | Reaction 2 | Reaction 3 |
|---|---|---|---|
| Initial T of water/solution(s) |  |  |  |
| Final T of solution |  |  |  |
| Volume of water/solution used |  |  |  |
| Mass of NaOH used |  |  |  |

## Analysis and Conclusions

Analysis Questions 1 – 5 are to be done for each of the three reactions. Show your work for reaction 1, then record the results for it and each of the other two reactions in the Summary Table.

1. Determine the change in temperature for the reaction.

2. Determine the number of moles of sodium hydroxide used in the reaction.

3. Determine the heat absorbed by the solution (which raises its temperature).

4. Determine the total heat released by the reaction.

5. Determine the heat evolved per mole of NaOH for the reaction.

# Report for Experiment 44

Name_____

## Summary Table

|  | Process 1 | Process 2 | Reaction 3 |
|---|---|---|---|
| Change in T ($\Delta T$) |  |  |  |
| Moles NaOH used |  |  |  |
| Heat absorbed by solution |  |  |  |
| Heat released in reaction |  |  |  |
| Heat evolved per mol NaOH |  |  |  |

**6.** Calculate the sum of $\Delta H_1$ and $\Delta H_3$. Find the difference between that sum and $\Delta H_2$.

**7.** Calculate the percent difference between $(\Delta H_1 + \Delta H_3)$ and $\Delta H_2$, using the following formula:

$$\% \text{ difference} = \frac{|(\Delta H_1 + \Delta H_3) - \Delta H_2| \, (100)}{\Delta H_2}$$

**8.** Refer to the net ionic equations that you wrote in the Prelaboratory assignment. Now, using Hess's Law, add the first and third equations together. Cancel any reaction species which appear on both sides of the equation. Compare the sum of those two equations to the second equation.

**9.** In Reaction 1, $\Delta H_1$ represents the heat evolved as solid NaOH dissolves. Look at the net ionic equations for the second and third reactions. In a few words, make similar statements about what each of the heats of reactions represents.

# Report for Experiment 44    Name_____

10. Suppose you had used 8.00 g of NaOH in Reaction 1. How would this have affected the change in temperature? Predict the heat that would have evolved in the reaction. What effect would increasing the mass of NaOH used have had on your calculation of $\Delta H_1$? Explain.

## Something Extra

1. Use chemical resources to learn some of the practical uses of NaOH.

2. What would have been the impact on your results if:
   a. the NaOH pellets that you used were contaminated with a nonreactive substance.

   b. you had mistakenly used 1 $M$ HCl rather than 2 $M$ in Reaction 3.

   c. you failed to stir the solutions in all three reactions.

3. Sodium hydroxide and hydrogen chloride are examples of substances which dissolve exothermically in water. Use chemical resources to identify at least two substances which dissolve endothermically in water.

# Report for Experiment 45

## Heats of Reaction and Hess's Law

### Prelaboratory Questions

**1.** Rewrite equation (3) of the Introduction in net ionic form.

**2.** Recopy equations (1) and (2) from the Introduction, but reverse equation (1), so that solid sodium hydroxide appears on the products side of the arrow and the dissolved ions appear as reactants. Now add the two equations just as you would in algebra class when solving two equations in two unknowns.

**3.** Show that the result you obtained by combining reversed equation (1) and equation (2) is identical to the net ionic equation for reaction (3).

**4.** All three reactions that you run in this experiment result in temperature increases. Are the reactions endothermic or exothermic? Explain.

# Report for Experiment 45     Name_____

**5.** You will use approximately 2.00 g of solid sodium hydroxide in two of the three reactions. Convert 2.00 g of NaOH to moles of NaOH.

## Data/Observations

### Data Table 1

|  | Reaction 1 | Reaction 2 | Reaction 3 |
|---|---|---|---|
| **Mass of foam cup** |  |  |  |
| **Initial T of water/solution(s)** |  |  |  |
| **Highest T of solution** |  |  |  |
| **Volume of water/solution used** |  |  |  |
| **Mass of NaOH used** |  |  |  |

## Analysis and Conclusions

**1.** Calculate q, the quantity of heat released by each of the reactions. Show your work. Be sure your answers are clearly identified and have the proper units.

  **Reaction 1**    Solid sodium hydroxide dissolves in water.

  **Reaction 2**    Solid sodium hydroxide reacts with 1.0 *M* acetic acid solution.

  **Reaction 3**    2.0 *M* sodium hydroxide reacts with 2.0 *M* acetic acid.

**2.** In the first two reactions, you used solid sodium hydroxide. Convert the actual masses of sodium hydroxide used to moles. Show your work.

# Report for Experiment 45

**Name**

3. The quantities and concentrations of the two solutions used in Reaction 3 were chosen so that 0.0500 moles of sodium hydroxide would be present. Use this information and the numbers of moles of NaOH you calculated in question **2** to convert your values of q from question 1 to $\Delta H$ values, in kJ/mol.

4. Recall that when you combined the equations for Reactions (1) and (2) in the second Prelaboratory Question, you reversed the direction of Reaction (1). If a reaction is exothermic in one direction, reversing the direction (products → reactants) changes the sign, but not the magnitude, of $\Delta H$. Use your results from question **3** to determine values for $\Delta H_1$, $\Delta H_2$, and $\Delta H_3$, as identified below. Watch signs and be sure to include appropriate units.

$$Na^+(aq) + OH^-(aq) \rightarrow NaOH(s) \qquad \Delta H_1$$

$$NaOH(s) + HC_2H_3O_2(aq) \rightarrow H_2O(l) + Na^+(aq) + C_2H_3O_2^-(aq) \qquad \Delta H_2$$

$$Na^+(aq) + OH^-(aq) + HC_2H_3O_2(aq) \rightarrow H_2O(l) + Na^+(aq) + C_2H_3O_2^-(aq) \quad \Delta H_3$$

5. Calculate the sum of $\Delta H_1$ and $\Delta H_2$. Show your work.

# Report for Experiment 45     Name_____

6. Because the sum of the first two equations of question 4 is the same as the third equation, the combined values of $\Delta H_1$ and $\Delta H_2$ should equal $\Delta H_3$. Determine the percent deviation between the sum of $\Delta H_1$ and $\Delta H_2$, and the value you obtained for $\Delta H_3$ by dividing the difference by the value for $\Delta H_3$. Note the absolute value signs in the equation.

$$\frac{|\{\Delta H_1 + \Delta H_2\} - \{\Delta H_3\}|}{\Delta H_3} \times 100\% =$$

7. In this experiment some loss of heat energy is unavoidable. Discuss some of the ways in which heat energy may not have been fully accounted for in this experiment.

Name_____

Section_____ Date_____

# Report for Experiment 46

## Sunprint Paper Photography

### Prelaboratory Questions

1. What determines the energy or color that is emitted when an object glows or emits electromagnetic radiation?

2. Oxidation-reduction reactions are defined as processes in which electrons are transferred from one substance to another. Why is light often responsible for initiating oxidation-reduction reactions?

3. Rank the following types of electromagnetic radiation in increasing order of wavelength and in increasing order of energy: ultraviolet light, yellow light, infrared radiation, x-rays, blue light, radio waves.

### Data/Observations

1. Note the colors that you observe at these points in the process:
   a. The color of the solution in Procedure - Day 1 - Step 3

   b. The color of the paper in Procedure - Day 2 - Step 2

   c. The color of the paper in Procedure - Day 2 - Step 3

# Report for Experiment 46

Name_____

    d.   The color of the paper in Procedure - Day 2 - Step 4

    e.   The color of the paper in Procedure - Day 2 - Step 5

## Analysis and Conclusions

1.  Attach one of your prints to this report sheet.

# Report for Experiment 46

Name_____

2. Day, place and time that the print was exposed:

3. Length of the time the print was exposed:

4. Weather conditions the day the paper was exposed (bright and sunny, slightly overcast, etc.):

5. In general, how can sunlight start a chemical reaction?

6. In the reaction in this experiment $Fe^{3+}$ ions are reduced to $Fe^{2+}$ ions. How does absorbed sunlight promote this process?

7. The $Fe^{2+}$ ions react with the ferricyanide ions to form an insoluble substance called Prussian blue. Why does the hidden part of the paper return to white after the photographic process is complete?

8. Most photographic work using light-sensitive paper must be done in a dark room. Would carrying out this experiment in a brightly-lit room be a problem?

# Report for Experiment 46

Name_____

9. How did the quality of your photograph compare to those of others?

## Something Extra

1. Design an experiment that uses sunprint paper to test the effectiveness of sunscreen products. After approval from your teacher, try it and see what happens.

2. Design an experiment that uses sunprint paper to test the effect of various types of incident light. Will the experiment work with fluorescent light? Incandescent light? A heat lamp?

3. Using chemical resources, find the formula of the Prussian blue molecule.

Name_____

Section_____ Date_____

# Report for Experiment 47

## Flame Tests

### Prelaboratory Assignment

1. Why must the nichrome wire be cleaned thoroughly after each flame test?

2. Why do we see colors in the flame tests, and why are there different colors for different metal ions?

### Data/Observations

| Salt solution | Observation |
|---|---|
| barium nitrate | |
| calcium nitrate | |
| copper(II) nitrate | |
| lithium nitrate | |
| potassium nitrate | |
| sodium chloride | |
| strontium nitrate | |

# Report for Experiment 47

Name_____

## Analysis and Conclusions

1. How does the flame test provide support for quantized energy levels? Explain your answer.

2. Fill in the table below.

| Unknown # | Observations | Metal ions present | Reason |
|-----------|-------------|--------------------|--------|
| 1 | | | |
| 2 | | | |

## Something Extra

Does the anion in a salt affect the color observed in a flame test? Design an experiment to answer this question, discuss it with your teacher, and try it.

# Report for Experiment 48

## Electron Probability

### Data/Observations

Fill in the following table:

| Ring Number | Average distance from target center (cm) | Area of ring (cm$^2$) | Number of hits in the ring | Number of hits per unit area (hits/cm$^2$) |
|---|---|---|---|---|
| 1 | 0.5 | 3.1 | | |
| 2 | 1.5 | 9.4 | | |
| 3 | 2.5 | 16 | | |
| 4 | 3.5 | 22 | | |
| 5 | 4.5 | 28 | | |
| 6 | 5.5 | 35 | | |
| 7 | 6.5 | 41 | | |
| 8 | 7.5 | 47 | | |
| 9 | 8.5 | 53 | | |
| 10 | 9.5 | 60 | | |

### Analysis and Conclusions

1. Which is the ring with the highest probability of finding a hit?



2. Which is the ring with lowest probability of finding a hit?

# Report for Experiment 48

Name_____

3. On the paper at the end of this report sheet construct a graph of the number of hits vs. average distance from the center.

4. On the paper at the end of this report sheet construct a graph of hits per unit area vs. average distance from the center. Use a different color than you used for the curve in **3**.

5. What does the graph of the number of hits vs. average distance represent? Account for its shape.

6. What does the graph of the hits per unit area vs. average distance represent? Account for its shape.

7. Is the maximum of each graph the same? Explain.

8. How well can we model an orbital with a dartboard and a dart? Specifically, focus on the following:
   a. Compare your target with Figure 11.15 in your text. How is it similar? How is it different?

# Report for Experiment 48

Name_____

**b.** Why do we predict an electron should be near the nucleus? Why do we expect the dart to land in the center of the target?

## Something Extra

How would changing the number of drops affect your results? Do the experiment with 10 drops and with 500 drops and compare your results.

# Report for Experiment 48

Name_____

Title: _____

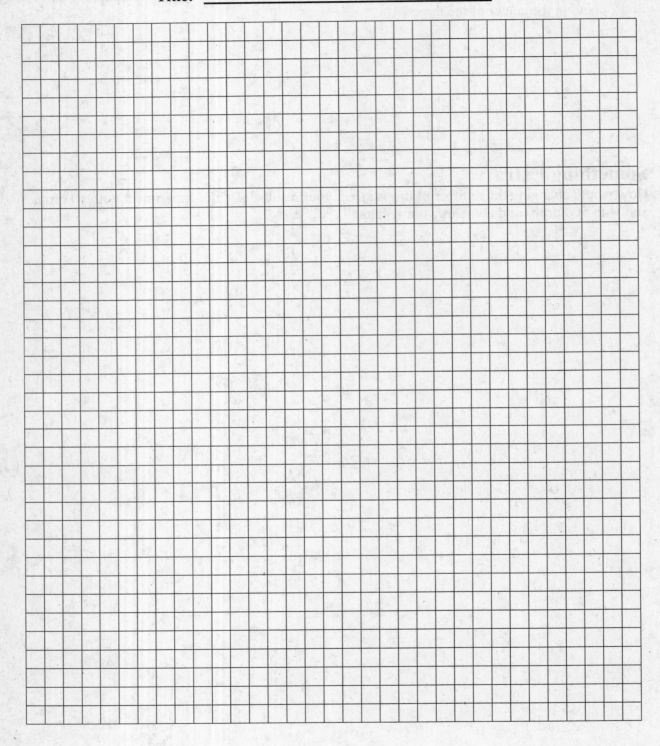

Name_____

Section_____ Date_____

# Report for Experiment 49

## Dyes and Dyeing

### Prelaboratory Questions

1. Cotton is pure cellulose, a type of carbohydrate. As such, it is essentially a long chain of carbon atoms with —C—O—H groups arranged along the chain.
   a. Would you expect the atoms in the —C—O—H group to be linear or bent? Explain.

   b. Make a sketch showing how hydrogen bonding could occur between the —C—O—H groups on neighboring molecules.

2. Wool is a protein, just as your hair is. Proteins contain many —NH groups on a long chain of carbon atoms. What sort of attractive forces occur between proteins and dye molecules? Explain.

3. The Introduction and Procedure mention that some dyes are polar molecules, while others are ionic. Which would you expect to form the strongest bonds?

### Data/Observations

Affix the strips you prepared to the right-hand edge of the paper. When your report is returned, they are yours to keep.

**Part 1**
**Step 1:** Dye used _____
Description of test strip

# Report for Experiment 49

**Name_____**

**Step 2 or 3:**    Dye used   _____
Description

**Step 4:**   Dye used   _____
            Mordant used  _____
Description

## Analysis and Conclusions

1. Consult the fabric list supplied by your teacher for the multifiber strips you used. Overall, which type of fabric seems the most effective at binding to the greatest number of dyes? Which is least effective? Account for the differences.

# Report for Experiment 49

**Name**_____

2. Answer either **a.** or **b.**, depending on which step you carried out.
   **a.** If you did step 2, describe and account for the effect of the vinegar rinse on your test strip. How might you reverse that change?
   **b.** If you did step 3, describe and account for the difference between the portions washed with soap and water only and the one washed with soap, water and bleach.

## Something Extra

1. In a reference book or on the internet, locate the structure of one of the dyes that you used. Copy the structure below and indicate several of the bonding sites that would help the dye molecule adhere to fabrics.

2. Use the internet or a reference book to locate the structural formulas of cellulose, nylon and any sort of protein structure (representing wool and silk). These molecules are large, often containing several thousand atoms. But, because they are polymers, they have variable sizes. Some individual fibers may be twice as long as others. This means that you will not be able to find an exact formula. On a separate paper show the unit structure for each molecule you found. Identify some of the polar and ionic sites on each molecule where bonding can occur. Use the nylon structure to explain why it is difficult to dye.

# Report for Experiment 50

## Models of Molecules

### Prelaboratory Questions

1.  Draw Lewis structures for each of the molecules given below. **Note:** In all of the molecules containing carbon, the carbon atom is the central atom.

    HCN                        $H_2CO$                        $CCl_2H_2$

    $O_3$                        $H_2S$                        $PH_3$

### Analysis and Conclusions

1.  Which shape has the longest distance between the ends of the toothpicks? Which shape has the shortest distance between the ends of the toothpicks?

2.  Group together molecules that have the same number of atoms coming off the central atom. Do these molecules have the same geometry? The same shape?

# Report for Experiment 50

Name_____

**3.** Group together models that have the same number of toothpicks coming off the central atom. Do these molecules have the same geometry?  The same shape?

**4.** What do the toothpicks represent?

**5.** Why do we position the ends of the toothpicks as far apart as possible?

**6.** Can we use the molecular formula to predict the shape of a small molecule?  Explain.

## Summary Table
Complete the table below:

| Molecule | Distance between ends of toothpicks | Bond angles | Electron pair geometry | Molecular Shape |
|---|---|---|---|---|
| HCN | | | | |
| $O_3$ | | | | |
| $CCl_2H_2$ | | | | |
| $H_2CO$ | | | | |
| $H_2S$ | | | | |
| $PH_3$ | | | | |

# Report for Experiment 50

**Name**_____

## Something Extra

In this activity, the greatest number of toothpicks in the central atom was four. Make models with five and six toothpicks in the central atom. Show these to your teacher.

# Report for Experiment 51

## Gas Laws and Drinking Straws

### Prelaboratory Questions

1. Read Section 13.1 in your text and explain how a barometer works in your own words.

### Data/Observations

1. Were you able to drink the water in Part 1?

2. Were you able to drink the water in Part 2?

3. How many drinking straws could you drink through in Part 3? What was the limiting height?

4. What happens to the water in the straw in Part 4 (careful observations are required)?

### Analysis and Conclusions

1. Explain your results in Part 1.

# Report for Experiment 51

Name_____

**2.** Explain your results in Part 2.

**3.** Compare your number of straws and heights from Part 3 with those of other groups.

**4.** Why is there a limit to the number of straw through which you can drink?

**5.** What is the maximum theoretical height through which you can drink? Why can't you drink from this height?

**6.** Explain your results in Part 4.

**Name_____**

**7.** Why can we drink through a straw?

## Something Extra

Does the diameter of a drinking straw affect the results of Part 4? Carry out an experiment to answer this question.

# Report for Experiment 52

## Determining Absolute Zero

## Prelaboratory Questions

1.  Under what conditions of temperature and pressure is a gas most ideal?

2.  If 740 mL of a gas are collected at 120°C, what volume will the gas occupy if the temperature is decreased to 10°C with the pressure remaining constant?

3.  A sample of a gas is collected and measured to be 100.0 mL at standard temperature and pressure.  At what Celsius temperature will its volume be twice as great?  Half as great? Assume constant pressure.

## Data/Observations

|  | Temperature | Height of Air in Tube |
|---|---|---|
| **Room Temperature** |  |  |
| **Ice water** |  |  |
|  |  |  |
|  |  |  |
|  |  |  |
|  |  |  |
|  |  |  |

# Report for Experiment 52

**Name**_____

## Analysis and Conclusions

1. Obtain a large piece of graph paper. You might cut a standard 8 1/2"x11" piece of graph paper lengthwise and tape the ends together, creating a 4 1/4" by 22" piece of paper.
2. Draw a horizontal axis along the long side near the bottom of the paper. The horizontal axis must allow for temperatures ranging from -300°C on the left to 100°C on the right. Locate the vertical axis at 0°C.
3. Plot the temperatures on the horizontal axis and the height of the air column on the vertical axis.
4. Draw the best straight line that fits the points. Extend your line (extrapolate) to the horizontal axis (where the height of air would be zero).
5. Identify the temperature where the line crosses the horizontal axis. What is your estimated value for absolute zero?

6. By how many degrees does your value differ from the accepted value? Is your answer too high or too low?

7. Should the slope of your line decrease or increase to make your results more accurate?

## Something Extra

1. The value of the bore of your capillary tube actually increases as the tube is heated. Does this affect your graph? Explain.

2. In this experiment, you are plotting height versus temperature rather than volume versus temperature. Explain why treating your data this way should still result in the same value for absolute zero.

3. Air is not an ideal gas. Does air actually have zero volume at absolute zero? Explain.

# Report for Experiment 53

# The *P-n* Relationship for Gases

## Prelaboratory Questions

1. Calculate the mass of baking soda that would generate enough carbon dioxide to exert 1.0-atm pressure in a 125-mL flask at 20°C. This is the maximum amount of baking soda that can be used in this experiment. Show your calculations in the space below.

2. Look up the solubility of carbon dioxide in water at 25°C and one atmosphere pressure in *The CRC Handbook of Chemistry and Physics*. Assuming that such a solution would have a density of 1.00 g/mL, calculate the molar solubility (mol $CO_2$/L of solution) of carbon dioxide at 25°C. Show your work.

3. a. Calculate the number of moles of carbon dioxide gas that would dissolve in 5.0 mL of water at 25°C. Assume the same molar solubility in vinegar as you calculated for water in Question 2. Show your work.

   b. What pressure would be exerted in 125-mL flask at 25°C by the number of moles of $CO_2$ that you calculated in Question 3a? This is the amount by which the pressure changes that you observe in the experiment will be reduced because some of the $CO_2(g)$ produced dissolves in the vinegar solution. Show your work.

# Report for Experiment 53

Name_____

## Data/Observations

(Extra spaces have been left for repeat trials)

Measured volume of flask: _____ mL (Optional)

| Trial | Mass NaHCO$_3$(s) | Initial Pressure | Final Pressure | Pressure CO$_2$ |
|-------|-------------------|------------------|----------------|-----------------|
| 1 | | | | |
| 2 | | | | |
| 3 | | | | |
| 4 | | | | |
| (5) | | | | |
| (6) | | | | |

## Analysis and Conclusions

1. For each trial you conducted, use the mass of sodium bicarbonate to calculate the moles of CO$_2$ generated. Show your work for Trial 1 and list the results for all trials in the space below.

Moles of CO$_2$:     Trial 1 _____

Trial 2 _____

Trial 3 _____

Trial 4 _____

2. On the grid at the end of this Report Sheet, make a plot of pressure of CO$_2$ *vs.* moles of CO$_2$. How closely does your line fit the ideal gas assumption that when $n = 0$, $P = 0$? Discuss. Attach the plot to this report.

# Report for Experiment 53

**3.** Convert your results from Question 1 to values for the ratio of pressure to moles of $CO_2$ for each trial, in L/mol. Calculate an average value, including average deviation. Show one sample calculation; enter your values.

**Pressure of $CO_2$/moles of $CO_2$:**   Trial 1_____

Trial 2_____

Trial 3_____

Trial 4_____

## Something Extra

**1.** What you have done so far, assumes that all of the carbon dioxide was present in the space above the mixture in the flask. In Prelaboratory Question 3a, you calculated the amount of $CO_2$ that would dissolve in the liquid in your flask; in 3b, you determined the amount by which the pressure readings would be in error.

  **a.** Adjust each of your values for the observed pressure of $CO_2$ by subtracting this pressure.

  **b.** Re-plot pressure *vs.* moles, as described in Question 2. Discuss the effect(s) this correction has on your results for Questions 2 and 3 of Analysis and Conclusions.

**2.** In reality, the solubility varies as the pressure of the $CO_2$ increases. This variation in solubility with pressure is known as Henry's Law. Consult an advanced text to see how you can determine the actual solubility for each of your experiments, then recalculate the corrected pressures that you found in the preceding question. Discuss the significance of your results.

# Report for Experiment 53

Name_____

### Pressure *vs.* Number of Moles of $CO_2$

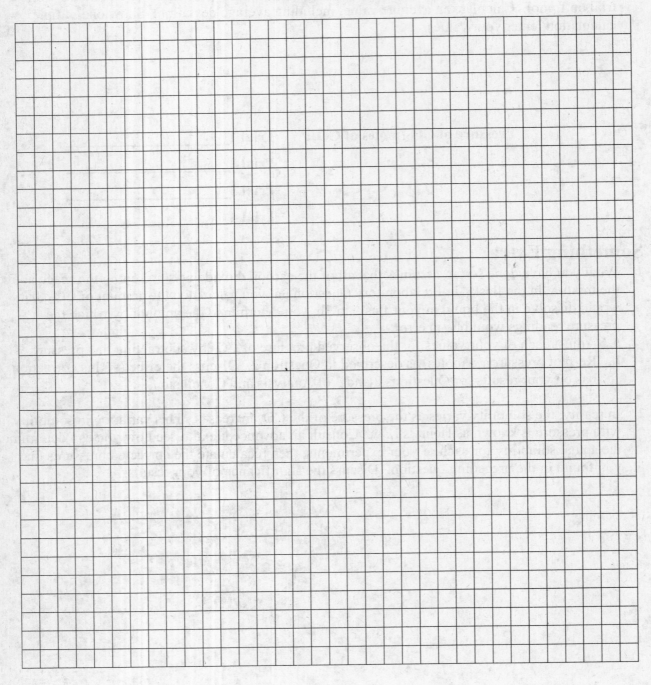

Name_____

Section_____ Date_____

# Report for Experiment 54

## Molar Volume and the Universal Gas Constant

### Prelaboratory Questions

1. Explain how the mass of a piece of magnesium ribbon may be calculated from its length and the mass of a 100.-cm strip of the same type of ribbon.

2. What two physical properties of hydrogen gas make it possible for you to collect it by displacement of water in your graduated cylinder?

3. Use Dalton's Law of Partial Pressures to explain why the pressure of hydrogen gas in the cylinder will be less than the observed barometric pressure in the laboratory. How will you determine the pressure of the hydrogen you produce?

4. Calculate the mass of baking soda, $NaHCO_3$, needed to neutralize 3.0 mL of 3.0 $M$ hydrochloric acid, $HCl(aq)$. Show your work; the answer alone is not enough. (**Hint:** the amount needed is less than 1 gram.)

5. The accepted value for the universal gas constant is 0.0821 L·atm /mol·K. What would it be if the pressure was measured in torr and the volume in milliliters? Show your calculation.

# Report for Experiment 54

**Name**_____

## Data/Observations

Mass of 100. cm of Mg ribbon          _____ g

       Barometric pressure          _____ atm

| **Experimental Data** | **Trial 1** | **Trial 2** | **Trial 3** |
|---|---|---|---|
| Length of Mg ribbon | _____cm | _____cm | _____cm |
| Volume of hydrogen collected | _____mL | _____mL | _____mL |
| Temperature of water | _____°C | _____°C | _____°C |
| Vapor pressure of water at experimental temperature | _____atm | _____atm | _____atm |

## Analysis and Conclusions

All of the calculations are to be shown for your first trial; you may simply report the results for the other two. Enter the results for all trials in the Summary Tables.

1. Calculate the mass of magnesium for each trial, using the mass of 1.00 m of Mg ribbon supplied by your instructor. Show your calculations here for Trial 1 (only) and enter the results in Summary Table 1.

2. Calculate the number of moles of magnesium used; enter the value for each trial in Summary Table 1. This is the same as the number of moles of hydrogen generated. (Why?)

# Report for Experiment 54    Name_____

3. Because you collected hydrogen over water, a small portion of the gas in the cylinder at the end of the reaction is water vapor; we say the hydrogen gas is "wet." The amount of water that evaporates is dependent only on the temperature, so it is a simple matter to determine the *partial pressure* of the water vapor in the graduate. Use the table of vapor pressures, found in Appendix A of your lab manual, to find the pressure due to water in the graduated cylinder. Subtract this value from the barometric pressure to get the pressure exerted by the "dry" hydrogen (hydrogen without the water vapor). Be sure to report the pressure to the correct degree of precision. Enter the results in Summary Table 1.

4. You have measured the volume occupied by a very small fraction of a mole of hydrogen, under a specific set of conditions of pressure and temperature. The volume occupied by one mole of gas is called the **molar volume** of the gas, and it is the same for all gases behaving ideally at a particular pressure and temperature. For each trial:
   a. Calculate the volume that 1.00 mole of hydrogen would occupy at your experimental temperature and pressure (called "laboratory conditions"). Record your answers in Summary Table 1.

   b. Use the combined gas law to calculate the volume that 1.00 mole of hydrogen would occupy at 1.00 atm and 273 K. (STP). Record your results in Summary Table 1.

# Report for Experiment 54

Name_____

## Summary Table 1

|  | Trial 1 | Trial 2 | Trial 3 |
|---|---|---|---|
| Mass of magnesium ribbon used | _____g | _____g | _____g |
| Moles of magnesium used | _____mol | _____mol | _____mol |
| Pressure of dry hydrogen | _____atm | _____atm | _____atm |
| Molar volume of $H_2$ (lab conditions) | _____L/mol | _____L/mol | _____L/mol |
| Molar volume of $H_2$ (STP) | _____L/mol | _____L/mol | _____L/mol |

5. Determine the value of $PV/nT$ for each trial. $P$ is the pressure of dry hydrogen, $V$ is the volume of gas collected, $T$ is the Kelvin temperature, and n is the number of moles of hydrogen generated. Enter these values in Summary Table 2.

6. Determine the average of your three values for $PV/nT$ and enter this in the last box of the first column of Summary Table 2. In similar fashion, determine the deviation for each of your three trials and the average deviation.

## Summary Table 2

|  | $PV/nT$ | Deviation |
|---|---|---|
| Trial 1 | _____ | _____ |
| Trial 2 | _____ | _____ |
| Trial 3 | _____ | _____ |
| Averages | _____ | _____ |

7. Your average for $PV/nT$ represents your experimental value for the universal gas constant, $R$. Calculate the percent error in your determination of the value of $R$.

_____% error

# Report for Experiment 55

## Magic Sand

### Prelaboratory Questions

1. What do we mean when we say that water "wets" a surface such as the surface of sand?

2. What is the difference between the way water "wets" the surface of a ten-year old car that has never been waxed, and the same car after it has been freshly waxed?

3. Water and sand can both form hydrogen bonds. How might this explain why wet sand clumps together?

# Report for Experiment 55

Name_____

## Data/Observations

| Part 1 | Magic Sand | Regular sand |
|---|---|---|
| **Dry substance** | | |
| Shape | | |
| Surface | | |
| Color | | |
| Other observations | | |
| **Wet substance** | | |
| Shape | | |
| Color | | |
| Surface | | |
| Stirred | | |
| Other observations | | |
| **After decanting** | | |
| Shape | | |
| Surface | | |
| Color | | |
| Other observations | | |

# Report for Experiment 55

**Name**_____

## Analysis and Conclusions

1. Write a paragraph explaining how Magic Sand differs from regular sand in its properties.

2. How did adding dishwashing detergent change the properties of Magic Sand? Explain.

Name_____

3. What is the major type of intermolecular forces present in water? How does Magic Sand interact with molecules that exhibit this type of intermolecular forces? How does regular sand interact with molecules that exhibit this type of intermolecular forces?

## Something Extra

Predict what would happen if Magic Sand were placed in vegetable oil. Explain why this would be different from what happened in this experiment. Try it and see if your prediction is correct.

Name_____

Section_____ Date_____

# Report for Experiment 56

## Freezing Point – a Physical Property

### Prelaboratory Questions

1. What is the difference between a physical and a chemical property?

2. On a molecular level what is occurring when a substance is cooled to the freezing point?

### Data/Observations

| Acetic Acid Time (minutes) | Freezing Temperature (°C) | Acetic Acid Time (minutes) | Melting Temperature (°C) |
|---|---|---|---|
| 0.0 | | 0.0 | |
| 0.5 | | 0.5 | |
| 1.0 | | 1.0 | |
| 1.5 | | 1.5 | |
| 2.0 | | 2.0 | |
| 2.5 | | 2.5 | |
| 3.0 | | 3.0 | |
| 3.5 | | 3.5 | |
| 4.0 | | 4.0 | |
| 4.5 | | 4.5 | |
| 5.0 | | 5.0 | |
| 5.5 | | 5.5 | |
| 6.0 | | 6.0 | |
| 6.5 | | 6.5 | |

# Report for Experiment 56

Name_____

| Acetic Acid Time (minutes) | Freezing Temperature (°C) | Acetic Acid Time (minutes) | Melting Temperature (°C) |
|---|---|---|---|
| 7.0 | | 7.0 | |
| 7.5 | | 7.5 | |
| 8.0 | | 8.0 | |
| 8.5 | | 8.5 | |
| 9.0 | | 9.0 | |
| 9.5 | | 9.5 | |
| 10.0 | | 10.0 | |
| 10.5 | | 10.5 | |
| 11.0 | | 11.0 | |
| 11.5 | | 11.5 | |
| 12.0 | | 12.5 | |
| 13.0 | | 13.0 | |
| 13.5 | | 13.5 | |
| 14.0 | | 14.0 | |
| 14.5 | | 14.5 | |
| 15.0 | | 15.0 | |

## Analysis and Conclusions

1.  Use the graph paper on the next page to carefully plot your data for the freezing of acetic acid. Draw a smooth curve through the freezing data points. Label the line.

2.  Use the graph paper on the next page to carefully plot your data for the melting of acetic acid. Draw a smooth curve through the melting data points. Label the line.

3.  What is the freezing point of pure acetic acid? How can you tell?

4.  What is the melting point of pure acetic acid?

5.  How do the freezing point and melting point of pure acetic acid compare?

# Report for Experiment 56

Name_____

## Something Extra

What happens to the freezing point of a pure substance when another substance is added to it? Add 0.5 g of benzoic acid crystals to your pure acetic acid and repeat the experiment. Was your prediction correct? Give an example of how this process can be used in everyday life.

# Report for Experiment 56

**Name**＿＿＿＿＿＿＿＿

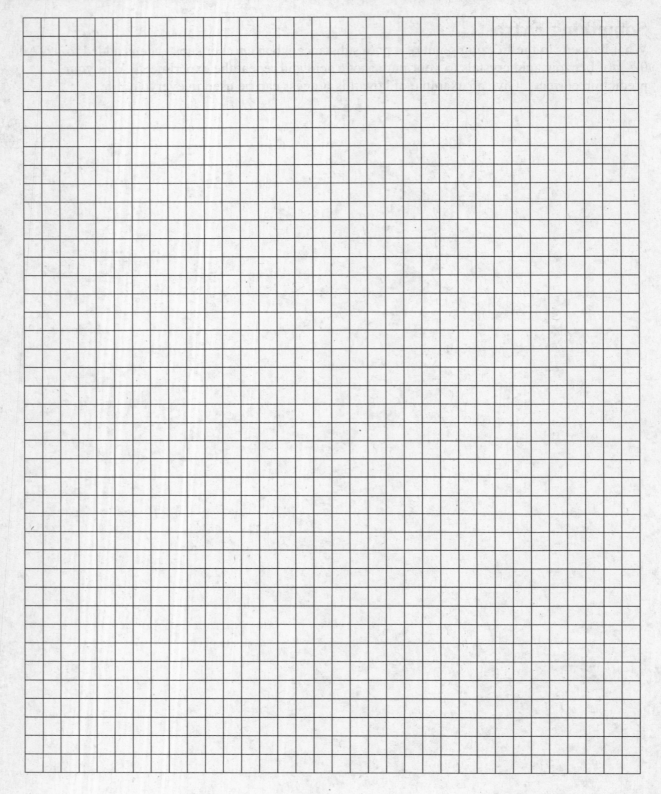

# Report for Experiment 57

## Heating and Cooling Behavior of a Pure Substance

### Prelaboratory Questions

1. What is the chemical structure of *para*-dichlorobenzene?

2. On a molecular level, what is the difference between a substance melting and a substance freezing? Between a substance melting and a substance vaporizing?

3. What happens to the molecules of a substance as it warms? What type of energy is involved?

### Data/Observations

**Cooling Behavior of *Para*-dichlorobenzene**

| Time (sec) | Temperature (*para*-dichlorobenzene) | Temperature (water) |
|---|---|---|
| 0 | | |
| 30 | | |
| 60 | | |
| 90 | | |
| 120 | | |
| 150 | | |
| 180 | | |
| 210 | | |
| 240 | | |
| 270 | | |
| 300 | | |
| 330 | | |
| 360 | | |

# Report for Experiment 57

Name_____

| Time (sec) | Temperature (*para*-dichlorobenzene) | Temperature (water) |
|---|---|---|
| 390 | | |
| 420 | | |
| 450 | | |
| 480 | | |
| 510 | | |
| 540 | | |
| 570 | | |
| 600 | | |

## Warming Behavior of *Para*-dichlorobenzene

| Time (sec) | Temperature (*para*-dichlorobenzene) | Temperature (water) |
|---|---|---|
| 0 | | |
| 30 | | |
| 60 | | |
| 90 | | |
| 120 | | |
| 150 | | |
| 180 | | |
| 210 | | |
| 240 | | |
| 270 | | |
| 300 | | |
| 330 | | |
| 360 | | |
| 390 | | |
| 420 | | |
| 450 | | |
| 480 | | |
| 510 | | |
| 540 | | |
| 570 | | |
| 600 | | |

# Report for Experiment 57

**Name**_____

## Analysis and Conclusions

1. Use a piece of graph paper to plot all of your data. Plot temperature along the vertical axis and time along the horizontal. Carefully calibrate your axes to use as much of the paper as possible.

2. Use a dot in a small circle for each point of the cooling data, and use a dot in a triangle for each point of the warming data. Use different colors for the water temperature data.

3. Plot all four lines of data on the same sheet of graph paper.

4. Draw a smooth curve through the warming data points. Draw a smooth curve through the cooling data points. Draw a smooth curve for each of the water temperature lines as well.

5. Label each line on your plot.

6. Describe the general appearance of your lines. What general trends do you notice?

7. From your graph, what is the freezing point of *para*-dichlorobenzene? How can you tell?

8. From your graph, what is the melting point of *para*-dichlorobenzene?

9. How do the freezing point and melting point compare?

# Report for Experiment 57

Name_____

10. What effect would increasing the amount of solid have on the shape of the melting or cooling graph?

## Something Extra

1. Use chemical resources to find the true melting point and freezing point of *para*-dichlorobenzene. How does your experimental result compare?

2. What is the significance of plotting the data for the water in both processes? Why does the *para*-dichlorobenzene data show different temperature behavior than the water lines?

3. What if pure substances are not really pure; that is, what if they are contaminated? What impact does contamination of a pure substance have on its melting or freezing point?

# Report for Experiment 58

## Heat of Fusion of Ice

### Prelaboratory Questions

1. You could have made volume measurements of the water and used the density of water as 1.0 g /mL to make your calculations. Why would this introduce error?

2. Why must excess ice be added? What problems might occur if this ice were not in excess?

### Data/Observations

1. What was the change in temperature of the water?

2. What was the mass of ice that melted?

### Analysis and Conclusions

1. Determine the heat transferred from the water to the ice.

2. According to your results, how much heat is required to melt a gram of ice?

# Report for Experiment 58

**3.** The actual value for the heat of fusion of ice is 330 J/g. Determine the percent error in your value.

**4.** Would each of the following scenarios cause you to calculate a heat of fusion higher or lower than the accepted answer?  Explain your answer.

**a.** The ice you add to the calorimeter has a significant amount of water on it.

**b.** The ice is initially colder than 0°C.

**c.** A significant amount of water is taken when the excess ice is removed from the calorimeter.

## Something Extra

We assume that all of the heat transfer in the calorimeter is from the water to the ice.  Design an experiment to determine the heat transferred to the environment surrounding the calorimeter.

# Report for Experiment 59

## Energy and Changes of State

### Prelaboratory Questions

1. Consider two solids. One has a melting point of 40°C, while the other melts at 60°C. What does this tell you about the relative strengths of the intermolecular forces present in each one?

2. What happens to the molecules of a substance when it changes from liquid to solid? Is freezing of a substance an endothermic process or an exothermic process?

### Data/Observations

The data are stored in your calculator. It will tell you what information is in what list. Use it or the graph to answer the questions in the next section. Unless your teacher directs you to do so, it is not necessary to transfer the data to your Report Sheet.

### Analysis and Conclusions

1. If they are available, use the program, Graphical Analysis™ and Graph-Link cables to transfer your data to a computer so that the graph can be printed and handed in with your report.

2. Describe the shapes of the two curves on your graph. Each shows time/temperature behavior, but one is for the water bath while the other is for the solid in the tube. On your printed graph, indicate which curve represents which substance. Include separate descriptions of the two graphs below.

# Report for Experiment 59     Name_____

3. As the salol changed from liquid to solid, its temperature was constant.
   a. At what temperature did this occur? The temperature at which you observed the plateau is the freezing point of salol, as determined by your experiment.

   b. What can you say about the kinetic energy of the salol molecules along the temperature plateau?

4. During the time that the temperature of the salol remained constant, the temperature of the water in the beaker continued to fall. Was this a change in kinetic energy or potential energy for the water? Explain.

5. During the same time period, the salol temperature was constant, however it must have been losing energy, also.
   a. Why _must_ it have been losing energy?

   b. If its temperature is constant, what type of energy must it have been losing? Explain.

6. While a liquid is boiling its temperature remains constant even though you continue to apply heat. How must the water be storing the energy you are adding? (In other words, is the heat energy that you add being used to increase the kinetic energy or the potential energy of the molecules?)

7. On the basis of your answer to question 6 explain why you would receive a more severe burn from steam at 100°C than you would from (liquid) water at 100°C.

Name_____

Section_____ Date_____

# Report for Experiment 60

## Vapor Pressure of Water
### An Experimental Determination

## Prelaboratory Questions

1. Write the ideal gas law:
   a. in standard form.



   b. rearranged to solve for $n$, in terms of $P$, $V$, and $T$.



   c. rearranged to solve for $P$, in terms of $n$, $V$, and $T$.



2. At any given temperature, what gas other than the trapped air is present in the inverted graduated cylinder?



3. State Dalton's Law of Partial Pressures. Explain how it applies to this experimental procedure.



## Data/Observations

1. Record your volume-temperature data in the first two columns of the Summary Table, which you will find at the top of the next page. The remaining columns will be filled in as you complete the Analysis and Conclusions section.

2. Record the barometric pressure here: _____ **torr**

## Analysis and Conclusions

1. The graduated cylinder was calibrated to be read in an upright position. To allow for the fact that your readings were made with the cylinder inverted, the volume should be corrected by subtracting 0.2 mL from each recorded value. Record the corrected volumes in the Summary Table.

# Report for Experiment 60

Name_____

## Summary Table

| Observed volume (mL) | Corrected volume (mL) | Temperature (K) | Moles of trapped air | Pressure of air (torr) | Pressure of $H_2O(g)$ (torr) |
|---|---|---|---|---|---|
| | | | | | |
| | | | | | |
| | | | | | |
| | | | | | |
| | | | | | |
| | | | | | |
| | | | | | |
| | | | | | |
| | | | | | |

2. Below 5° C, the vapor pressure of the water is negligible, so at this point we assume that the only gas in the graduated cylinder is the trapped air. We can further assume that the pressure in the cylinder is equal to the barometric pressure. Use these assumptions and the Ideal Gas Law to calculate the number of moles, *n*, of air in the graduated cylinder. Show a sample calculation.

3. Use your volume measurements for each of the other temperatures and the value of *n* obtained in question **2** to calculate the pressure due to air at each of the other temperatures. Answers will be *less than* the barometric pressure, since at each of these temperatures the graduated cylinder contains both air and water vapor. Show a sample calculation here.

4.  At each of the temperatures, the difference between the calculated pressure (from question **3**) and the barometric pressure is the vapor pressure of water at that temperature. For each temperature enter the atmospheric pressure, the pressure due to air, and the vapor pressure of water in the appropriate columns of your table. Show a sample calculation here.

5.  Plot vapor pressure as a function of temperature on the graph paper that follows this report sheet. Draw the best smooth-curve fit you can.

6.  Compare your results with the accepted values and curve shape, as found in your text or other reference. Discuss your findings.

# Report for Experiment 60

**Name**_____

**Title:** _____

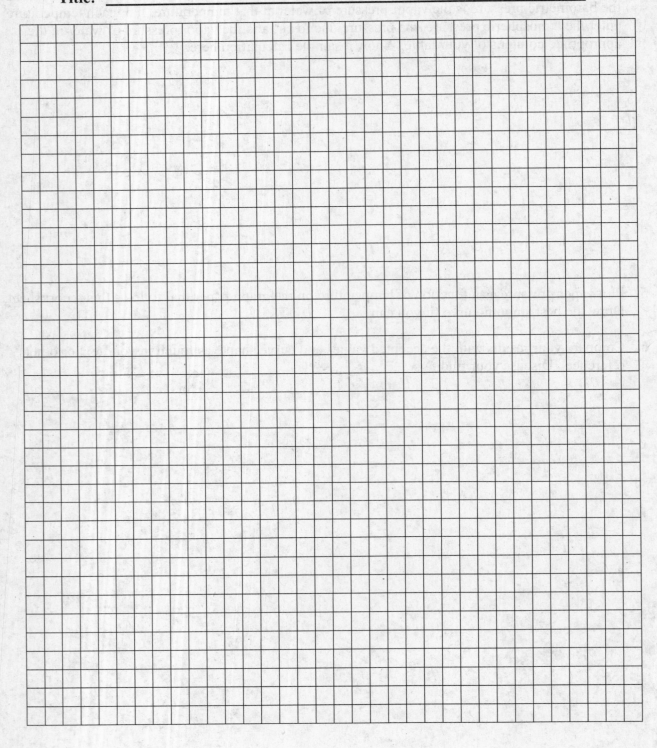

Name_____

Section_____ Date_____

# Report for Experiment 61

## Solution Properties

### Prelaboratory Questions

**1.** How can you determine which substance is the solvent and which is the solute in a solution?

**2.** How can you determine if two liquids are immiscible?

**3.** What is the difference between a saturated and an unsaturated solution?

### Data/Observations

**Part 1     Solubility**

Water-petroleum ether test tube

Iodine –water test tube

# Report for Experiment 61

Name_____

Liquids:

Test tube 1

Test tube 2

Test tube 3

## Part 2     Solubility

| Time for fine salt crystals to dissolve | s |
|---|---|
| Time for coarse salt crystals to dissolve | s |
| Time for salt crystals to dissolve in hot water | s |

| Mixtures | Stoppered and shaken | Heated and shaken | Cooling |
|---|---|---|---|
| Test tube 1 + 2 | | | |
| Test tube 3 + 4 | | | |

# Analysis and Conclusions

**Part 1     Solubility**

1. Which liquid is more dense, petroleum ether or water?  Support your answer with evidence.

2. Are petroleum ether and water miscible?  Support your answer with evidence.

3. Is iodine more soluble in water or petroleum ether?  How can you tell?

4. Which of the pairs of liquids in step 4 are miscible?

# Report for Experiment 61

Name_____

**Part 2    Rate of Dissolving**

1. Did the coarse salt dissolve faster or slower than the fine salt?

2. Did the salt dissolve faster in hot or cold water?

3. If salt is soluble in water why could you see a layer of dissolved salt at the bottom of the beakers in step 4?

4. Which of your test tubes in step 5 containing 1.0 g salt per 5 mL water were unsaturated?

5. Which test tube(s) containing 2.4 g salt per 5 mL water are saturated at room temperature?

6. Which salt is least soluble at higher temperature?

7. Classify the salt solutions at the higher temperature as:
   Unsaturated
   Saturated

8. Did the salt solutions which were unsaturated at higher temperature become saturated as they cooled?  Give evidence to support your answer.

9. If two liquids in a container are immiscible how can you tell which is which?

# Report for Experiment 61

Name_____

**10.** What do you conclude about particle size and rate of dissolving from your experiment in step 1?

**11.** What do you conclude about temperature and dissolving from your experiment in step 4?

**12.** Write a paragraph summarizing your conclusions regarding temperature and unsaturation.

## Something Extra

Suppose you were given a mixture containing sodium chloride and benzoic acid, both fine white crystals. Design a procedure to allow you to separate the two. Benzoic acid is soluble in hot water but not in cold water.

Name_____

Section_____ Date_____

# Report for Experiment 62

## Polar and Nonpolar Solvents

### Prelaboratory Questions

**1.** Why is it so important to thoroughly clean and dry the tubes before beginning Step 6?

**2.** Based on your previous experiences with copper(II) chloride and other compounds containing the copper(II) ion, how will you be able to tell whether $CuCl_2$ has dissolved or not (other than by the disappearance of crystals)?

**3.** Copper(II) chloride and ammonium nitrate are ionic compounds. Urea and isopropyl alcohol are weakly polar, while vegetable oil and naphthalene are completely nonpolar. Prepare a table predicting the solubility of each of the eight solutes in each of the two solvents, water and hexane.

# Report for Experiment 62

Name_____

4. Make a sketch showing the attractions of water molecules for each other. Indicate the attractive forces by dashed lines.




5. Make separate sketches indicating the attractive forces between water molecules and
   a. anions                                                    b. cations.




## Data/Observations

Enter your observations in the spaces below. In each case, indicate whether the solute was very soluble (vs), slightly soluble (ss), or insoluble (i).

| Solute | Behavior in water | Behavior in hexane |
|---|---|---|
| Copper(II) chloride, $CuCl_2$ | | |
| Urea, $H_2N-CO-NH_2$ | | |
| Sucrose, $C_{12}H_{22}O_{11}$ | | |
| Ammonium nitrate, $NH_4NO_3$ | | |
| Naphthalene, $C_{10}H_8$ | | |
| isopropyl alcohol, $CH_3-CH(OH)-CH_3$ | | |
| ethanol, $CH_3CH_2OH$ | | |
| Vegetable oil | | |

# Report for Experiment 62

**Name**_____

## Analysis and Conclusions

1. Divide the solutes into two or three groups, as follows. One group should include any solutes that dissolve only in water. The second group is for those solutes that dissolve only in hexane. If any solutes showed at least some solubility in both hexane and water, they constitute a third group.

**Group 1**

**Group 2**

**Group 3**

2. What similarities can you find for those solutes in your first group (water–soluble only)? In particular, look for structural characteristics.

3. Look up the structures of the solutes in your second group (hexane-soluble). If they are available, examine models of these molecules. Use the molecular shapes, and the arrangement and electronegativities of the atoms in the molecules to help you explain their solvent preference.

**Name_____**

4. Finally, for those solutes that had some affinity for both water and hexane:
   a. Try to identify the structural characteristics that attract them to water. Sketch the molecules and indicate the water attracting regions on your sketch.

   b. Now try to identify the part(s) of the same molecules that make them soluble in hexane. As with question 3, molecular models may make your task much easier. Sketch the molecules and indicate the hexane attracting (or water repelling) regions on your sketch.

# Report for Experiment 63

## Temperature and Solubility

### Prelaboratory Questions

1. Write the complete ionic equation for dissolving potassium nitrate in water.

2. Make a molecular level sketch of the potassium nitrate solution. Include a representation of the interactions of the water molecules and the ions. Name and describe the forces at work in this system.

### Data/Observations

| Test tube | (1) Mass of $KNO_3$ | (2) Mass of $H_2O$ | (3) $\frac{g\ KNO_3}{g\ H_2O}$ | (4) Crystallization Temp ($^\circ$C) | (5) Concentration of solution (g/100g $H_2O$) |
|---|---|---|---|---|---|
| A |  |  |  |  |  |
| B |  |  |  |  |  |
| C |  |  |  |  |  |
| D |  |  |  |  |  |

### Analysis and Conclusions

1. Use the data from column (3) of the data table to determine the concentration of each saturated solution in grams of solute per 100 grams of water. Show your calculation for tube A below, then record all concentrations in column (5) of the table.

# Report for Experiment 63     Name_____

2. On the graph paper at the end of this report sheet, plot the solubility of $KNO_3$ in grams/100. g of water vs. temperature. (Temperature is the horizontal axis.) Label the axes of your graph and give it an appropriate title. Draw the best smooth-curve through the points, extending your graph from 0°C to 100°C.

3. **Using your graph**, determine the solubility of $KNO_3$ (in g/100 g $H_2O$) at:
   **a.** 30°C          **b.** 70°C          **c.** 0°C          **d.** 90°C

4. **From your graph**, determine the temperature at which each of the following mixtures of potassium nitrate in water would be saturated solutions.
   **Note:** Use your graph; do not calculate the values.

   **a.** 45 g $KNO_3$ in 100. g $H_2O$          **b.** 20 g $KNO_3$ in 100. g $H_2O$

   **c.** 25 g $KNO_3$ in 25 g $H_2O$          **d.** 100 g $KNO_3$ in 250. g $H_2O$

5. Define the terms, *saturated, unsaturated,* and *supersaturated* as they apply to solutions. Use complete sentences.
   saturated:



   unsaturated:



   supersaturated:



6. Classify the following solutions as saturated, unsaturated, or supersaturated, based on your graph. Defend your answers. Note that **c.** and **d.** require you to convert from the concentrations given to g/100 g $H_2O$ before you refer to your graph.

   **a.** 75 g $KNO_3$/100. g $H_2O$ at 40°C          **b.** 60 g $KNO_3$/100. g $H_2O$ at 50°C

   **c.** 100 g $KNO_3$/75 g $H_2O$ at 80°C          **d.** 175 g $KNO_3$/250. g $H_2O$ at 40°C

# Report for Experiment 63

Name_____

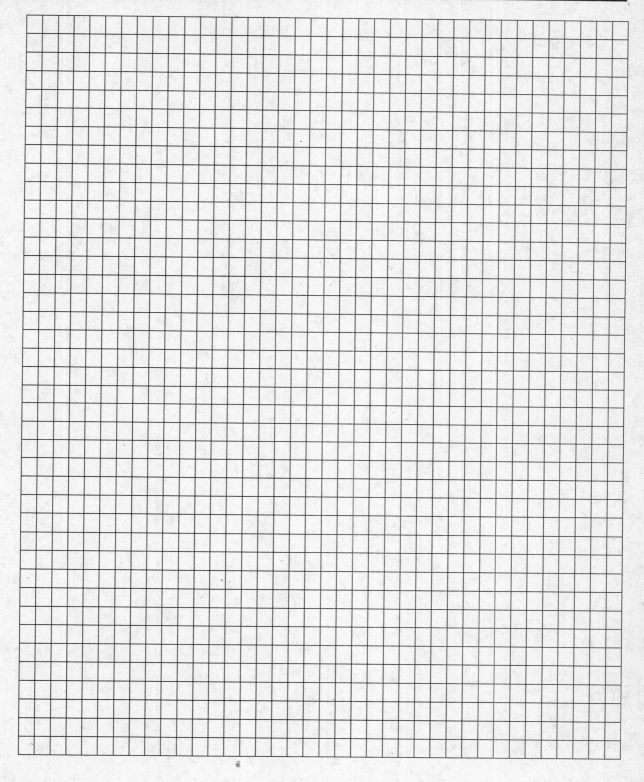

Name_____

Section_____ Date_____

# Report for Experiment 64

## Chloride in Water

### Prelaboratory Questions

1. Provide balanced net ionic equations for all chemical reactions in this lab.

2. What is the purpose of titrating solutions of potassium chloride with known concentrations?

3. What is the purpose of diluting the potassium chloride solutions and titrating them?

4. Provide calculations for all dilutions to be made in this lab.

### Analysis and Conclusions

1. Determine the percent error for each of the three titrations in Part 1 by comparing the known chloride concentrations to those you found by titration.
   Titration 1:

   Titration 2:

   Titration 3:

# Report for Experiment 64

Name_____

2. Which known concentration of potassium chloride gave the smallest percent error? Was this expected? Explain.

3. Compare your school sample and bottled water results with your classmates. Are they similar?

## Summary Tables
### Part 1: Determining Accuracy of the Titration

| | 10.0 mL 5.00 x $10^{-3}$ $M$ KCl($aq$) |
|---|---|
| initial buret reading | |
| final buret reading | |
| volume 5.00 x $10^{-3}$ $M$ AgNO$_3$ | |

| | 10.0 mL 5.00 x $10^{-4}$ $M$ KCl($aq$) |
|---|---|
| initial buret reading | |
| final buret reading | |
| volume 5.00 x $10^{-4}$ $M$ AgNO$_3$ | |

| | 10.0 mL 5.00 x $10^{-5}$ $M$ KCl($aq$) |
|---|---|
| initial buret reading | |
| final buret reading | |
| volume 5.00 x $10^{-4}$ $M$ AgNO$_3$ | |

# Report for Experiment 64

**Name**_____

## Part 2: Testing Water Samples

|  | 10.0 mL home water |
|---|---|
| initial buret reading |  |
| final buret reading |  |
| volume 5.00 x $10^{-3}$ $M$ AgNO$_3$ |  |

|  | 10.0 mL home water |
|---|---|
| initial buret reading |  |
| final buret reading |  |
| volume 5.00 x $10^{-4}$ $M$ AgNO$_3$ |  |

|  | 10.0 mL school water |
|---|---|
| initial buret reading |  |
| final buret reading |  |
| volume 5.00 x $10^{-3}$ $M$ AgNO$_3$ |  |

|  | 10.0 mL school water |
|---|---|
| initial buret reading |  |
| final buret reading |  |
| volume 5.00 x $10^{-4}$ $M$ AgNO$_3$ |  |

|  | 10.0 mL bottled water |
|---|---|
| initial buret reading |  |
| final buret reading |  |
| volume 5.00 x $10^{-3}$ $M$ AgNO$_3$ |  |

# Report for Experiment 64          Name_____

| | 10.0 mL bottled water |
|---|---|
| initial buret reading | |
| final buret reading | |
| volume 5.00 x 10$^{-4}$ $M$ AgNO$_3$ | |

Calculate the chloride ion concentration for the home sample, school sample, and bottled water sample and report the results in the table below.

| | using 5.00 x 10$^{-3}$ $M$ silver nitrate | using 5.00 x 10$^{-3}$ $M$ silver nitrate |
|---|---|---|
| home sample | | |
| school sample | | |
| bottled water | | |

## Something Extra
Contact your local water company and the bottled water distributor and obtain data on the chloride ion concentrations. Do these agree with your results?

Name_____

Section_____ Date_____

# Report for Experiment 65

## Hard Water Analysis

### Prelaboratory Questions

1. Water softeners remove cations such as $Ca^{2+}$ and $Mg^{2+}$ from the water, but they must also replace these cations with less troublesome cations such as $Na^+$. Why?

2. One of your four beakers will serve as a control. What does that mean?

3. The final color of the titration vessels (A-C) is often a lighter shade of blue than the control. Why?

4. Notice that Procedure steps 2 and 3 direct you to put tap water in beakers A-C, *then* put distilled water in beaker D. Suggest a reason why it would not be good to fill the control beaker first, then fill the titration vessels.

### Data/Observations

**Number of drops of EDTA used for control beaker D:** _____

**Titration Data:**

| Beaker | Drops of EDTA used |
|--------|--------------------|
| A      |                    |
| B      |                    |
| C      |                    |
| D      |                    |

**Note:** If additional titrations were conducted, show the results in the space above.

# Report for Experiment 65

Name_____

## Calibration Data:

Water level before adding EDTA     _____mL

Water level after adding EDTA     _____mL

## Analysis and Conclusions

1. Use your calibration data from Procedure Part 2 to determine the number of drops that is equivalent to 1.00 mL. Show your calculations below.

2. Convert the number of drops you used in each titration to milliliters. Enter the results of your calculations here.

| Beaker | Drops of EDTA | mL of EDTA |
|--------|---------------|------------|
| A | | |
| B | | |
| C | | |
| D | | |

3. Calculate the number of moles of EDTA used in each titration, using the volumes you calculated in the previous question and the molar concentration of the EDTA, 0.010 M. Show a sample calculation for Beaker A .

| Beaker | Mol EDTA |
|--------|----------|
| A | |
| B | |
| C | |
| D | |

4. Given that one EDTA reacts with one calcium ion, calculate the number of grams of calcium that were present in each of your 5.00 ml samples. Show a sample calculation for Beaker A.

| Beaker | Grams $Ca^{2+}$ |
|--------|-----------------|
| A | |
| B | |
| C | |
| D | |

# Report for Experiment 65

**Name**_____

5.  Assuming the density of water to be 1.0 g/mL (or 1000 g/L), a calcium ion concentration of 1.0 g/L would correspond to 1.0 g $Ca^{2+}$/1000 g water or 1000 g $Ca^{2+}$/ 1,000,000 g water or 1000 ppm (parts per million). Convert the results of question 4 from grams of $Ca^{2+}$ per 5.00 g of $H_2O$ to grams of $Ca^{2+}$ per million grams of water( ppm). Show your calculation for Beaker A, then enter the results for all three in the spaces below. Report both the individual sample values and the average value for the three trials.

### Calcium concentration:

| Beaker | ppm $Ca^{2+}$ |
|--------|---------------|
| A | |
| B | |
| C | |
| D | |
| Average | |

6.  Identify two major sources of experimental error in this analysis and suggest ways the procedure could be modified to minimize those errors.

## Something Extra

1.  If you have (or if someone you know has) a water softener in the home, *and* if you can do so without seriously disrupting the operation of the system, try taking samples for analysis (about 40-50 mL) of both the softened and the unsoftened water. (A good way to do this is to draw your "unsoftened" sample from an outdoor tap-this water is usually not run through the water softener.) Analyze at least three samples of each; discuss the significance of your results. It might be interesting to do this just before and just after the softener has been 'recharged' with salt.

2.  If your kitchen (or other) faucet has a purification filter, try analyzing both the filtered and the unfiltered water. Discuss your results as outlined in #1.

3.  Repeat the experiment as described in the Procedure, but use 2 mL of water and 1 mL of buffer, instead of 5 mL and 2 mL, respectively. Compare both the hardness values obtained and the consistency (precision) of data, and discuss your findings.

4.  Try substituting volumes of 10 mL for the water and 4 mL of buffer in the original procedure. Discuss as suggested in **#3**.

Name_____

Section_____ Date_____

# Report for Experiment 66

## Acids and Bases

### Prelaboratory Questions

1. Chocolate and coffee can have bitter tastes. With what class of compounds would you associate these two foods?

2. Cite at least two examples of foods (other than citrus fruit products) that you know must contain acids.

3. Based on your reading of Chapter 16, what is the net ionic reaction that occurs when any strong acid reacts with a strong base?

4. Explain the meaning of the word "strong" in relation to acids and bases.

### Data/Observations

For each of the questions posed in the Procedure, describe the process you followed and what observations you made. If you need more paper, add it.

**Question:**
1. What happens when strong acids come into contact with active metals?

# Report for Experiment 66

**2.** Are strong acids and bases strong electrolytes? How is conductivity related to concentration?

**3.** Is it possible to distinguish experimentally between strong and weak electrolytes on the basis of conductivity?

**4.** If you add an indicator to a sample of a strong acid, what happens to the color of the indicator as you dilute the acid?

# Report for Experiment 66

Name_____

5. How do indicators respond when you start with a fixed amount of a strong acid and add strong base to it, one drop at a time?

6. Do all indicators give the same results in an experiment such as the one you designed for Part 5?

7. In what way (or ways) do weak acids and bases differ from the stronger ones in the various tests you've done here?

8. Is your school's tap water neutral?

# Report for Experiment 66

Name_____

## Analysis and Conclusions

Answer each of the eight questions, citing evidence from your observations to support your answers.

1. What happens when strong acids come into contact with active metals?

2. Are strong acids and bases strong electrolytes? How is conductivity related to concentration?

3. Is it possible to distinguish experimentally between strong and weak electrolytes on the basis of conductivity?

4. If you add an indicator to a sample of a strong acid, what happens to the color of the indicator as you dilute the acid?

5. How do indicators respond when you start with a fixed amount of a strong acid and add strong base to it, one drop at a time?

# Report for Experiment 66

**Name_____**

6. Do all indicators give the same results in an experiment such as the one you designed for Part 5?

7. In what way (or ways) do weak acids and bases differ from the stronger ones in the various tests you've done here?

8. Is your school's tap water neutral?

Name_____

Section_____ Date_____

# Report for Experiment 67

## Acid Rain

## Prelaboratory Questions

1. Provide calculations for all dilutions to be made in this lab.

## Data/Observations

**Part 1**

|                       | rainwater sample |
| --------------------- | ---------------- |
| initial buret reading |                  |
| final buret reading   |                  |
| volume of NaOH        |                  |

**Part 2**

|                       | rainwater sample |
| --------------------- | ---------------- |
| initial buret reading |                  |
| final buret reading   |                  |
| volume of NaOH        |                  |

**Part 3**

|                       | (sample) |
| --------------------- | -------- |
| initial buret reading |          |
| final buret reading   |          |
| volume of NaOH        |          |

# Report for Experiment 67

Name_____

## Analysis and Conclusions

**Part 1:**

1. What is the number of moles of NaOH used in the titration?

2. What is the number of moles of acid in your rainwater sample?

3. Determine the concentration of $H^+$ in your rainwater sample.

4. Calculate the pH of your rainwater sample

5. Collect class data.

# Report for Experiment 67

Name_____

**Parts 2 and 3**

6. Determine the pH of rainwater after it flows through untreated soil.

7. Determine the pH of rainwater after it flows through soil mixed with calcium carbonate.

8. What is the normal range of pH for rainwater?  Use class data.

9. Does the untreated soil neutralize the rainwater?

10. Does soil mixed with calcium carbonate neutralize the rainwater?

11. Which soil (untreated or mixed with calcium carbonate) neutralized the rainwater better?

# Report for Experiment 67

**Name**_____

## Something Extra

1. Does boiling affect the pH of rainwater? Boil and cool rainwater and test it. Explain your results.

2. Does potting soil have an effect on the pH of rainwater? Test it and compare your results to the soil you gathered.

Name_____

Section_____ Date_____

# Report for Experiment 68

## Indicators

### Prelaboratory Questions

1. Suppose the instructions told you to empty the contents of the well plate into a waste beaker at the conclusion of Part 1 of the procedure. Do you think that the solution in the waste beaker will be acidic, basic, or neutral? Give a reason for your prediction.

2. Describe a way to test your hypothesis from Prelaboratory Question 1, using only the materials provided for this experiment.

### Data/Observations
**Part 1**

| Solution Tested | Congo Red | Indigo Carmine | Bromcresol Purple | Phenol-phthalein | Universal Indicator |
|---|---|---|---|---|---|
| Hydrochloric acid | | | | | |
| Acetic acid | | | | | |
| Ammonia | | | | | |
| Sodium Hydroxide | | | | | |

# Report for Experiment 68

Name_____

## Part 2

| Indicator Tested | Drops NaOH needed | Color of Univ. Ind. | Approx. pH |
|---|---|---|---|
| Congo Red | | | |
| Indigo Carmine | | | |
| Bromcresol Purple | | | |
| Phenolphthalein | | | |

## Analysis and Conclusions

1. Answer the following questions, based on your data and on your knowledge of acids and bases. Some questions may have more than one correct answer; if more than one indicator will accomplish a particular task, list all those that will. In each case, justify your choices by citing evidence from the data table.

   a. Which of the four indicators could be used to tell a strong acid from a strong base?

   b. Which of the four indicators could be used to tell a weak acid from a weak base?

   c. Which of the indicators (if any) could be used to tell a strong acid from a weak acid?

   d. Which of the indicators (if any) could be used to tell a strong base from a weak base?

2. Use the color chart provided for the Universal Indicator to estimate the approximate initial pH of each of the acid and base solutions you used.

   Hydrochloric acid    _____    Acetic acid    _____

   Ammonia solution    _____    Sodium hydroxide    _____

3. Use your information from Part 2 to determine the approximate pH range in which each of the four indicators from Part 2, Step 2 changes color.

   Bromcresol Purple    _____    Congo Red    _____

   Indigo Carmine    _____    Phenolphthalein    _____

4. Use your results from Part 2 to explain your conclusions from Part 1.

Name_____

Section_____ Date_____

# Report for Experiment 69

## Analysis of Vinegar

### Prelaboratory Questions

1. Write the equation for the reaction between acetic acid and NaOH. Use the structural formula for acetic acid, found in Chapter 16. In the formulas of the reactants, circle the atoms that form water.

2. What is the purpose of the indicator? How does it tell you when a titration is complete?

3. Give two reasons for **Safety Special Note #2**. (**Hint:** Consider both your own experiment and that of the person who uses the balance after you.)

4. What does the parenthetical expression ($\pm$ 0.001 g) mean in Step 1 of Part 1 of the Procedure?

5. Read Step 4 of Part 1 of the Procedure. Answer the question that appears in parentheses.

### Data/Observations

#### Data Table 1
Mass of empty beaker

_____ g

Mass of beaker and NaOH pellets

_____ g

Mass of empty, dry graduated cylinder

_____ g

Mass of graduated cylinder and NaOH solution

_____ g

# Report for Experiment 69

## Data Table 2

| Mass of Vinegar Pipet (g) | | Mass of NaOH Pipet (g) | |
|---|---|---|---|
| Before titration 1 | _____ g | Before titration 1 | _____ g |
| After titration 1 | _____ g | After titration 1 | _____ g |
| Before titration 2 | _____ g | Before titration 2 | _____ g |
| After titration 2 | _____ g | After titration 2 | _____ g |
| Before titration 3 | _____ g | Before titration 3 | _____ g |
| After titration 3 | _____ g | After titration 3 | _____ g |
| Before titration 4 | _____ g | Before titration 4 | _____ g |
| After titration 4 | _____ g | After titration 4 | _____ g |

## Analysis and Conclusions

Samples of all calculations are to be shown in the spaces provided.

### Part 1

1. Calculate the mass of sodium hydroxide used in preparing your solution. Convert this to moles.

2. Determine the molarity of your sodium hydroxide solution.

3. Determine the mass of the sodium hydroxide solution you prepared, then use that mass to determine the density of your sodium hydroxide solution.

4. Calculate the concentration of the NaOH solution in moles of NaOH per gram of solution.

# Report for Experiment 69

**Name**_____

## Part 2

### Table 3

| Mass of Vinegar Used (g) | | Mass of NaOH Used (g) | |
|---|---|---|---|
| Titration 1 | _____ g | Titration 1 | _____ g |
| Titration 2 | _____ g | Titration 2 | _____ g |
| Titration 3 | _____ g | Titration 3 | _____ g |
| Titration 4 | _____ g | Titration 4 | _____ g |

5. From your data, calculate the mass of NaOH solution used, the number of moles of NaOH used, and the number of moles of acetic acid that must have been present for each of your four titrations. Show your work for trial 1; enter the results for all four titrations in Data Table 4.

### Table 4

| **Titration 1:** | | **Titration 2:** | |
|---|---|---|---|
| NaOH solution used (g) | _____ g | NaOH solution used (g) | _____ g |
| Moles of NaOH used | _____ mol | Moles of NaOH used | _____ mol |
| Moles of $HC_2H_3O_2$ in vinegar sample | _____ mol | Moles of $HC_2H_3O_2$ in vinegar sample | _____ mol |

| **Titration 3:** | | **Titration 4:** | |
|---|---|---|---|
| NaOH solution used (g) | _____ g | NaOH solution used (g) | _____ g |
| Moles of NaOH used | _____ mol | Moles of NaOH used | _____ mol |
| Moles of $HC_2H_3O_2$ in vinegar sample | _____ mol | Moles of $HC_2H_3O_2$ in vinegar sample | _____ mol |

6. Determine the mass of acetic acid present in each of your four titration samples. Then find the percent of acetic acid in each vinegar sample, by dividing the mass of acetic acid present by the mass of vinegar used. Convert the decimal fraction to a percent. Present your results in the Summary Table. Show the calculations for Trial 1 in the space below.

# Report for Experiment 69

Name_____

## Summary Table

|  | Titration 1 | Titration 2 | Titration3 | Titration 4 |
|---|---|---|---|---|
| mol $HC_2H_3O_2$ | mol | mol | mol | mol |
| mass of vinegar | g | g | g | g |
| mass % of acetic acid in vinegar | % | % | % | % |

7. Calculate an average value for the mass percent of acetic acid in the vinegar you analyzed. Base your average on the three trials that show the closest agreement; omit the trial that deviates most greatly from the others.

8. Calculate the deviation from the average for each of the four trials, then calculate the average deviation for the three trials that show the best agreement.

9. Report the mass percent of acetic acid in the vinegar as a percent ± average deviation.

# Report for Experiment 69

**Name**_____

10. Assuming the density of white vinegar to be 1.0 g/mL, calculate:
   a. the mass of 1.0 L of white vinegar;

   b. the mass of acetic acid in 1.0 L of vinegar;

   c. the number of moles of acetic acid in 1.0 L of vinegar; and

   d. the molar concentration (molarity) of acetic acid in white vinegar.

## Something Extra

Sodium hydroxide reacts with the moisture and carbon dioxide in the air, so it is very likely that the mass you reported in question 1 of Analysis and Conclusions is not all sodium hydroxide. Find out how to use potassium acid phthalate, KHP, to standardize a sodium hydroxide solution. Then, with your teacher's permission, repeat the experiment, this time standardizing the solution before proceeding to Part 2.

Name_____

Section_____ Date_____

# Report for Experiment 70

## Quantitative Titration

### Prelaboratory Questions

1.  Determine the number of grams of NaOH needed to make 100.0 mL of a 1.00 $M$ NaOH solution.

2.  If 24.3 mL of 0.085 $M$ NaOH solution are needed to completely neutralize 15.5 mL of an unknown acid, what is the concentration of the acid solution?

3.  What is the $[H^+]$ in each of the following acid solutions?
    a. 0.004 $M$ $HNO_3$

    b. 1.33 $M$ $HClO_4$

    c. 12 $M$ HI

### Data/Observations

Identity of unknown acid _____

Molarity of NaOH_____

Titration #1
    volume of acid solution used
    initial volume of NaOH solution in buret    _____
    final volume of NaOH    _____

Titration #2
    volume of acid solution used    _____
    initial volume of NaOH    _____
    final volume of NaOH    _____

Titration #3
    volume of acid solution used    _____
    initial volume of NaOH    _____
    final volume of NaOH    _____

# Report for Experiment 70     Name_____

## Analysis/Conclusions

1. For each of the three titrations, determine the number of milliliters of NaOH required to reach the end point.

   Titration #1

   Titration #2

   Titration #3

2. Calculate the molarity of the unknown acid in each of the three samples.

   Titration #1

   Titration #2

   Titration #3

3. Determine the average molarity of the unknown acid. Report your average answer to three significant digits.

4. What effect would each of the following have on the molarity of your acid solution:
   a. Rather than the desired light pink color, a bright magenta color marked the endpoint of the titration

   b. Ten drops of phenolphthalein, rather than 6-8, were used in the titration

   c. The flask was not swirled during the titration, and the experiment was stopped at the first sign of pink

# Report for Experiment 70

Name_____

## Something Extra

1.  Using chemical resources, investigate other common indicators. Do all indicators change color at the same pH?

2.  Repeat this experiment to compare the amount of acid in lemon juice, orange juice, or grapefruit juice samples (or in various types of vinegar). Report your findings.

3.  Using chemical resources, identify the primary acid found in each of the following:
    a.  aspirin
    b.  vinegar
    c.  milk

# Report for Experiment 71

## Conductivity Titration – a CBL Investigation

### Prelaboratory Questions

1. The equation for the reaction you are investigating is given in molecular form in the Introduction. Present the same reaction as:

   a. a complete ionic equation (assume the oxalic acid dissociates into two hydrogen ions and a oxalate ion).

   b. a net ionic equation.

2. Why is it necessary to filter out the precipitated solid remaining after the completion of the experiment?

3. The lead(II) acetate solution has an approximate concentration of 0.010 $M$. What volume of 0.10 $M$ oxalic acid will be needed to reach the equivalence point? Show calculations to defend your prediction.

# Report for Experiment 71

## Data/Observations

1. Using either the TRACE function, or STAT/EDIT from your calculator, complete the table below.

| Volume of $H_2C_2O_4$ (mL) | Conductivity Reading |
|:---:|:---:|
| 0.00 | |
| 0.50 | |
| 1.00 | |
| 1.50 | |
| 2.00 | |
| 2.50 | |
| 3.00 | |
| 3.50 | |
| 4.00 | |
| 4.50 | |
| 5.00 | |

2. Use graph paper (below) to plot your data of conductivity *vs*. volume of $H_2C_2O_4$. Assume that the lines showing the conductivity are straight. Extend each so that the two intersect. The intersection point is your experimental value for the equivalence point of the reaction. Be sure to label the axes.

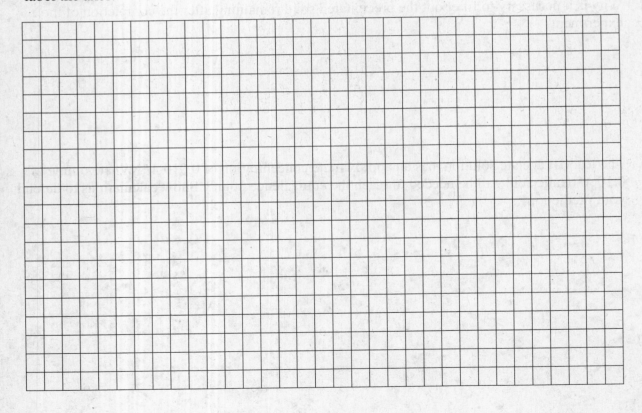

# Report for Experiment 71

**Name**_____

## Analysis and Conclusions

1. Describe the shape of the curve. Include a description of the relative slopes of the two intersecting lines.

2. Identify the volume of $H_2C_2O_4$ that was needed to reach the equivalence point (this need not be a whole number).

Volume of $H_2C_2O_4$ for equivalence _____

3. Compare the value from the preceding question with your prediction in **Prelaboratory Question 3**. Suggest a possible explanation for any significant difference.

4. There are two products to the reaction: lead(II) oxalate, which is insoluble, and acetic acid which is a weak electrolyte. Account for the fact that once the equivalence point is reached, the conductivity increases again.

# Report for Experiment 71     Name_____

## Something Extra

1. As you add the oxalic acid and precipitate the lead(II) ion from solution as $PbC_2O_4(s)$, you are not changing the total amount of lead(II) ion present in the system.

   a. Use the volume and molarity of the oxalic acid to determine the number of moles of oxalate ion added at the equivalence point.

   b. The result you got in **part a.** must also be the number of moles of lead(II) ion that were originally present. Why?

   c. Use the number of moles of lead(II) ion that were originally present in the 20.0 mL of the 0.010 $M$ lead(II) acetate solution to calculate the actual molarity of lead(II) acetate solution.

Name_____

Section_____ Date_____

# Report for Experiment 72

## Acids, Bases, and Buffers

### Prelaboratory Questions

1. Calculate the mass of sodium acetate you would need to prepare 30.0 mL of 0.10 $M$ $NaC_2H_3O_2$ solution. Show your calculations.

2. Acids are proton donors; bases are proton acceptors. In these definitions, the "protons" are actually hydrogen ions. Why are hydrogen ions referred to as protons?

3. Ammonia is a weak base. Write the net ionic equation for the reaction in which an ammonia molecule accepts a proton (hydrogen ion) from water.

### Data/Observations

If you used CBL, you can get the data from List 1 and List 2 (L1 and L2), by selecting STAT/EDIT.

pH of 0.10 $M$ $NaC_2H_3O_2$ _____

# Report for Experiment 72

Name_____

| Volume of NaOH (mL) | Part 1 pH | Part 2 pH |
|---|---|---|
| 0.00 | | |
| 10.00 | | |
| 15.00 | | |
| 20.00 | | |
| 25.00 | | |
| 26.00 | | |
| 27.00 | | |
| 28.00 | | |
| 29.00 | | |
| 30.00 | | |
| 31.00 | | |
| 32.00 | | |
| 33.00 | | |
| 34.00 | | |
| 35.00 | | |

**Part 3**

| Volume of HCl (mL) | Distilled water pH | Buffer mixture pH |
|---|---|---|
| 0.00 | | |
| 1.00 | | |
| 2.00 | | |
| 3.00 | | |
| 4.00 | | |
| 5.00 | | |

## Analysis and Conclusions

1. Plot your data for each of the two titrations (Parts 1 and 2) on the accompanying graph paper.

2. Describe the difference between the shapes of the graphs for the buffered and unbuffered systems with sodium hydroxide.

# Report for Experiment 72

**Name**_____

3. Account for the effect of small quantities of a strong acid on the buffered system. Why does the pH not change as rapidly for the buffer as it did for distilled water? What was consuming the acid?

4. Write equations for:
   a. the reaction that occurred in the titrations in Part 1 and 2. (**Hint:** it is the same reaction in both cases.)

   b. the reaction that occurred when HCl was added to the buffer in Part 3.

## Something Extra

Write an equation that accounts for the pH of the sodium acetate solution.

Title: _____

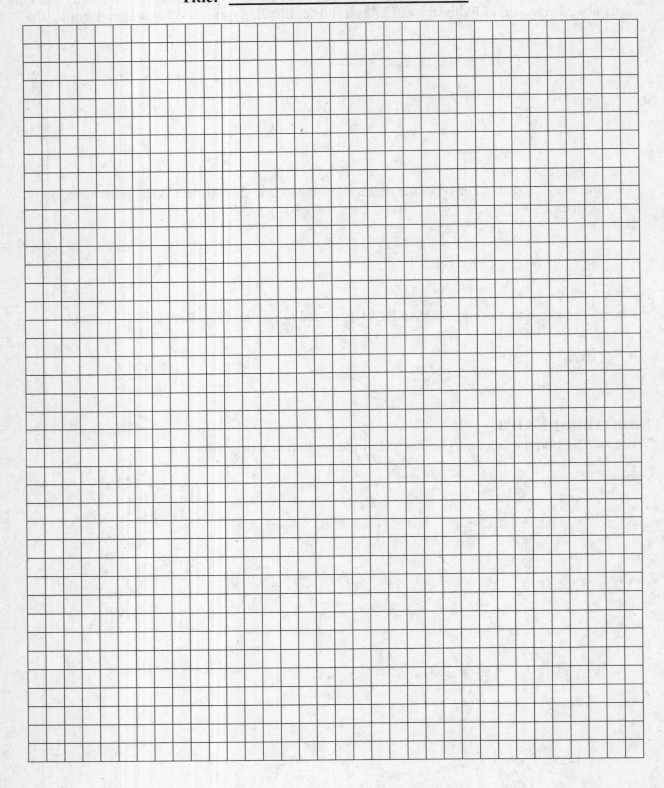

# Report for Experiment 73

## Iodine Clock Reaction

### Prelaboratory Questions

1. On a molecular level, why should more concentrated solutions react more quickly than less concentrated ones?

2. On a molecular level, why should warm solutions react more quickly than cooler ones?

3.  a. You are to prepare a solution by mixing 10.0 mL of 0.02 $M$ $KIO_3$ with 10.0 mL of water. What is the final concentration of the $KIO_3$ in your diluted solution?

    b. Suppose that you are preparing another solution by mixing 25.0 mL of 0.033 $M$ $KIO_3$ with 18.0 mL of 0.50 $M$ $H_2SO_4$. What is the final concentration of the $KIO_3$ in your solution?

# Report for Experiment 73

Name_____

## Data/Observations

**Part 1     The Effect of Concentration Changes**

Time required for control reaction _____

**Data Table 1**

| mL A | Time (s) |
|------|----------|
| 10.0 | |
| 9.0 | |
| 8.0 | |
| 7.0 | |
| 6.0 | |
| 5.0 | |
| 4.0 | |
| 3.0 | |
| 2.0 | |
| 1.0 | |

**Part 2     The Effect of Temperature Changes**

Time required for control reaction _____

| Temperature Range (°C) | Time (s) |
|------------------------|----------|
| 0 – 5 | |
| 10 – 15 | |
| 20 – 25 | |
| 30 – 35 | |
| 40 – 45 | |
| 50 - 55 | |

## Analysis and Conclusions

**Part 1**

1.  The concentration of solution A is 0.02 *M*.  How many moles of $KIO_3$ are in each milliliter of solution A?

# Report for Experiment 73

**Name**_____

2. Calculate the concentration of $KIO_3$ in moles per liter for each of the solutions after all the components have been mixed.

3. Plot a graph of the concentration-time data by plotting concentration of $KIO_3$ (or milliliters of A) on the vertical axis and plotting time on the horizontal axis. Connect the points with a smooth line.

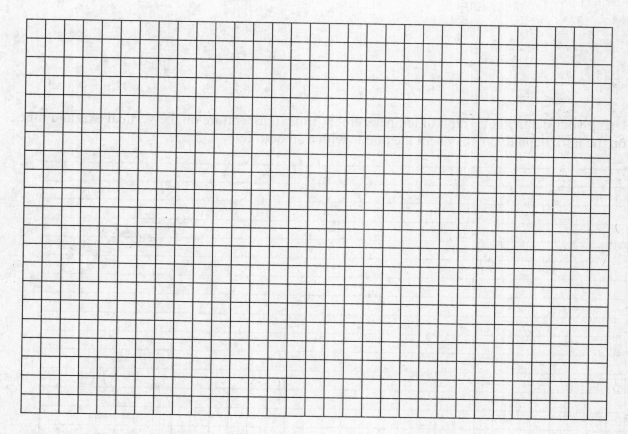

4. Why is it important to keep the total volume at 10.0 mL during the dilutions of solution A?

# Report for Experiment 73

Name_____

5. What generalizations can you make concerning the effect on the time of the reaction resulting from varying the concentration of solution A?

6. How is the time of a reaction related to the rate of that reaction?

**Part 2**

1. Using your data, plot a graph of temperature *vs.* time (temperature on the vertical axis and time on the horizontal axis). Connect the points with a smooth line.

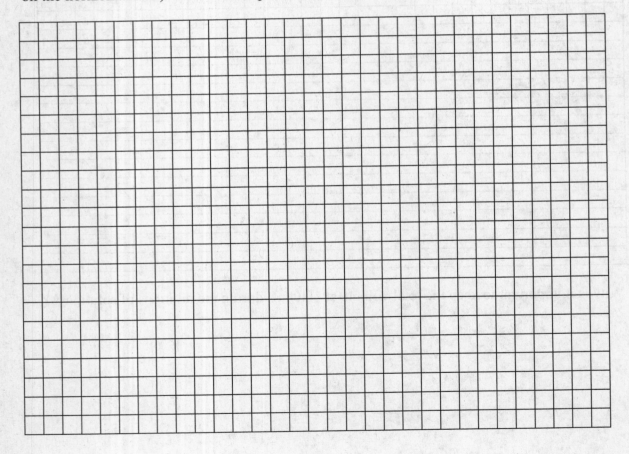

# Report for Experiment 73

Name_____

2. What general relationship can you derive from the graph?

3. Make a prediction of the time the reaction should have taken at 0°C and 75°C.

## Something Extra

1. Use chemical resources to investigate other "clock reactions" in chemistry, such as the "Old Nassau" reaction.

2. Comment on the difference in the shapes of the two lines you plotted.

Name_____

Section_____ Date_____

# Report for Experiment 74

## Equilibrium Beads

### Prelaboratory Questions

1. How will you tell when equilibrium is established?

2. Why must the agitator be careful to always shake the box at the same rate?

### Data/Observations

1. Report the time to reach equilibrium in each part.
   Part 1:

   Part 2:

### Analysis and Conclusions

1. Compare your times required to reach equilibrium with those of other groups.

2. Compare your values of $K$ with those determined by other groups.

# Report for Experiment 74

Name_____

3. Should you expect the same value of $K$ for Part 1 and Part 2? What causes differences in $K$ values?

4. Should you expect the same value of $K$ for each group in a given part? What causes differences in $K$ values?

5. How does this activity show that equilibrium is microscopically dynamic but macroscopically static?

6. List some differences between this activity and a chemical system achieving equilibrium.

# Report for Experiment 74

**Name**_____

## Summary Table

**Part 1**

| Time | Number of "A" particles | Number of "A$_2$" particles | Value for $Q$ |
|------|------|------|------|
| Initial | | | |
| 1 minute | | | |
| 2 minutes | | | |
| 3 minutes | | | |
| 4 minutes | | | |
| 5 minutes | | | |
| 6 minutes | | | |
| 7 minutes | | | |
| 8 minutes | | | |
| 9 minutes | | | |
| 10 minutes | | | |

# Report for Experiment 74

Name_____

**Part 2**

| Time | Number of "A" particles | Number of "B" particles | Number of "AB" particles | Value for $Q$ |
|---|---|---|---|---|
| Initial | | | | |
| 1 minute | | | | |
| 2 minutes | | | | |
| 3 minutes | | | | |
| 4 minutes | | | | |
| 5 minutes | | | | |
| 6 minutes | | | | |
| 7 minutes | | | | |
| 8 minutes | | | | |
| 9 minutes | | | | |
| 10 minutes | | | | |

## Something Extra

How would different numbers of beads affect the results? Carry out an experiment to answer this question.

Name_____

Section_____ Date_____

# Report for Experiment 75

## Equilibrium and Le Chatelier's Principle

### Prelaboratory Questions

1.  The formula for solid cobalt(II) chloride is $CoCl_2 \cdot 6H_2O$. What name do we give to compounds which have water molecules bound to them?

2.  a.  Write the equation for dissolving calcium chloride in water.

    b.  Use Le Chatelier's Principle to predict the effect of addition solid calcium chloride to a solution containing both of the cobalt complexes.

3.  a.  Write the equation for dissolving silver nitrate in water.

    b.  Write the equation for the precipitation reaction that you would expect when a solution containing silver ions is added to a solution containing chloride ions.

### Data/Observations

Initial appearance of solid cobalt(II) chloride hexahydrate:

Color of solution produced by adding solid $CoCl_2 \cdot 6H_2O$ to alcohol:

Effect of adding water to alcoholic solution of cobalt(II) chloride:

# Report for Experiment 75     Name_____

Describe the changes caused in each of the vials in Step 6:

Vial 1  Addition of 12 $M$ HCl($aq$)

Vial 2  Addition of $CaCl_2(s)$

Vial 3  Addition of acetone, $(CH_3)_2CO$

Vial 4  Addition of $AgNO_3(aq)$

Describe the effects of heating and cooling the mixture that you prepared in Step 7.

## Analysis and Conclusions

The net-ionic equation for the equilibrium reaction you have been investigating is

$$Co(H_2O)_6^{2+}(aq) + 4Cl^-(aq) \rightleftharpoons CoCl_4^{2-}(aq) + 6H_2O(l)$$

         pink                                          blue

1. **a.** Which cobalt complex was favored by addition of water to the solution of cobalt(II) chloride in alcohol?

   **b.** Use Le Chatelier's Principle to explain the color change you observed.

2. **a.** Which cobalt complex was favored in both procedure 6a and 6b?

   **b.** What ion is common to both of the reagents you used to bring about the color changes in these two steps?

   **c.** Use Le Chatelier's Principle to explain why the color changes occurred in each case.

               

# Report for Experiment 75

**Name**_____

3. Acetone absorbs water. Use this fact and Le Chatelier's Principle to explain the color change that you saw when you added acetone to the third vial in Step 6.

4. Silver chloride, AgCl, is a white solid. For the equilibrium

$$Ag^+(aq) + Cl^-(aq) \rightleftharpoons AgCl(s)$$

the value of the equilibrium constant is $K = 6 \times 10^9$.

   a. At equilibrium, would you expect to have mostly silver and chloride ions in solution, or mostly solid silver chloride? Explain.

   b. What color was the solid you formed in Step 6d? What must it have been?

   c. What color did the liquid in the vial turn? Which complex of cobalt was favored? Explain.

   d. Use Le Chatelier's Principle to explain why the liquid in the vial underwent the color change.

5.   a. Which cobalt complex was favored by addition of heat? Which complex was favored by cooling?

   b. Rewrite the equation for the reaction, including the energy term in the equation. The value of $\Delta H$ for the process is +50kJ/mol.

   c. Use Le Chatelier's Principle and the equation from **5b** to explain the color changes that resulted from the heating and cooling.

# Report for Experiment 76

## Chemical Equilibrium

### Prelaboratory Questions

1. Why is chemical equilibrium dynamic on a molecular level?

2. In a particular chemical reaction, solution A reacts with solution B to produce solution C. Solution A is colorless, solution B is light blue, and solution C is intensely pink. This reaction reaches equilibrium and gives a light purple color. How would you expect the color of this solution to change if you added more solution A? Explain your answer briefly.

3. In a particular reaction, $X + 2Y \rightarrow XY_2$. If you begin with 3 $M$ X and 4 $M$ Y, and if at equilibrium 40% of the reactants have become products, how much of each species will you expect to find at equilibrium? What is the equilibrium constant for the reaction?

4. A solution of $Fe(NO_3)_3$ is 0.200 $M$. If you measure 10.0 mL of that solution and then dilute it to 25 mL with water, what is the resulting concentration of the $Fe(NO_3)_3$?

# Report for Experiment 76

Name_____

## Data/Observations

Depth of solutions when color intensities are the same:

Vial 1 _____          Vial 2 _____

Vial 1 _____          Vial 3 _____

Vial 1 _____          Vial 4 _____

Vial 1 _____          Vial 5 _____

## Analysis and Conclusions

Show a sample calculation for each of the questions 1-6, and then record your results in the Summary Table at the end of this report.

1. Determine the initial concentration of $Fe^{3+}$ in each vial.

2. Determine the initial concentration of $SCN^-$ in each vial.

3. Determine the ratio of the depths of the solutions in the vials. Express this as the depth in Vial 1 divided by the depth in Vial n.

4. Determine the equilibrium concentration of the $FeSCN^{2+}$ in each vial.

5. Determine the equilibrium concentration of the $Fe^{3+}$ in each vial.

# Report for Experiment 76

**Name_____**

6. Determine the equilibrium concentration of the SCN⁻ in each vial.

7. Using expressions **(a)**, **(b)**, and **(c)** that are found at the bottom of the Summary Table, and using your calculated values for the equilibrium concentrations of $FeSCN^{+2}$, $Fe^{+3}$, and SCN⁻, calculate the answers for each "constant".

8. Only one of the expressions **(a)**, **(b)**, and **(c)** accurately represents the expression for an equilibrium constant. To determine which of those expressions resulted in the most "constant" constant, divide the largest answer in each column by the smallest answer in the column. The column that shows the number closest to 1 best represents the true equilibrium expression.

## Summary Table

| Vial | $[Fe^{3+}]_{initial}$ | $[SCN^-]_{initial}$ | Ratio of Depths | $[FeSCN^{2+}]_{equil}$ | $[Fe^{3+}]_{equil}$ | $[SCN^-]_{equil}$ | (a) | (b) | (c) |
|------|------|------|------|------|------|------|------|------|------|
| 1 | | | | | | | | | |
| 2 | | | | | | | | | |
| 3 | | | | | | | | | |
| 4 | | | | | | | | | |
| 5 | | | | | | | | | |

(a) $\dfrac{[Fe^{3+}][SCN^-][FeSCN^{2+}]}{[Fe^{3+}][SCN^-]} =$ 
(b) $\dfrac{[FeSCN^{2+}]}{[Fe^{3+}][SCN^-]} =$

(c) $\dfrac{[Fe^{3+}] + [SCN^-]}{[FeSCN^{2+}]} =$

Largest/Smallest

Name_____

Section_____Date_____

# Report for Experiment 77

## MOM and Your CBL

### Prelaboratory Questions

1. Why do the labels on these antacids always tell you to shake the bottle well before using?

2. Write the dissociation equations for aluminum hydroxide and magnesium carbonate in water. Does the position of equilibrium lie more strongly to the left or the right? Defend your choice.

3. Using the appropriate equation, apply Le Chatelier's Principle to explain why a compound such as magnesium hydroxide, which has very low solubility in water, will nevertheless dissolve well in the presence of acid.

### Data/Observations

**Data Table**                                              Antacid used:_____

| Trial | Initial pH | Minimum pH | 10-second pH | Final pH | Remarks |
|-------|-----------|-----------|-------------|----------|---------|
| 1 | | | | | |
| 2 | | | | | |
| 3 | | | | | |
| 4 | | | | | |
| 5 | | | | | |

**Appearance of mixture after final trial:**

# Report for Experiment 77

Name_____

## Analysis and Conclusions

1. Describe the shapes of the graphs you produced. Offer an explanation for the observed decrease in pH, followed by a return to nearly the original level. In other words, what caused the decrease, and why does the pH then increase again?

2. Notice that the pH drops very rapidly, but returns slowly to a value near the initial one (except, perhaps, for the final trial).

   a. Addition of acid to a slurry of milk of magnesia causes a sharp reduction; why?

   b. The return to higher pH is much slower than the initial drop. Why? What must happen for the pH to rise? (**Hint:** Two things must occur.)

3. It is likely that the mixture in the beaker turned clear after the last trial. What does that signify about the nature of the mixture?

4. Examine the values in the "Final pH" column. Account for the consistency of the values. (**Hint:** What did the mixture look like after each trial?)

5. Gram for gram, which would you expect to be the most effective antacid: magnesium hydroxide or aluminum hydroxide? (**Hint:** How many moles of hydroxide ion is present in one gram of each compound?)

6. Gaviscon™ uses both aluminum hydroxide and magnesium carbonate. How do these two compare, gram for gram, as neutralizers?

Name_____

7. Look up values for the solubility product constants, $K_{sp}$, for magnesium hydroxide, aluminum hydroxide, and magnesium carbonate. Suppose you were to repeat the procedure using just one of the three compounds, rather than the commercial products. Speculate as to how the relative $K_{sp}$ values might influence the shape of the pH *vs*. time curves you made.

## Something Extra

1. Repeat the experiment using a different antacid. Compare the two sets of results.

2. Compare name brands (such as Phillips, Maalox) with store brands containing the same active ingredients.

3. Test your predictions from **Analysis question #7.**

Name_____

Section_____ Date_____

# Report for Experiment 78

## Oxidation and Reduction

### Prelaboratory Questions

1. **a.** What are the most common ionic charges for the elements shown in their ionic compounds?

   Aluminum                                    Oxygen

   **b.** Complete the following equations, showing aluminum metal and oxygen gas forming the ions you identified in **part a of this question**.
   **i.**    $Al(s) \rightarrow$             +

   **ii.**    $O_2(g) +$    $\rightarrow$    2

   **c.** Identify each of the equations in **part b.** as oxidation or reduction.

2. Write the balanced equation for the reaction between aluminum metal and oxygen gas to form aluminum oxide.

3. Identify each of the following processes as an example of oxidation, or reduction, or both.
   **a.** Chlorine gas forms chloride ion.

   **b.** Sodium metal forms sodium ions.

   **c.** Iron rusts.

   **d.** Hydrogen peroxide breaks down into water and oxygen gas. **(Hint:** the oxygen in hydrogen peroxide, $H_2O_2$, has an oxidation state of -1.)

   **e.** Household bleach removes a stain from an article of clothing.

## Data/Observations

**Part 1**   Describe the reaction between magnesium and hydrochloric acid.

# Report for Experiment 78

Name_____

**Part 2** Describe the reaction (if any) between:
copper(II) nitrate and zinc

zinc nitrate and copper

**Part 3** Describe the effect on $KMnO_4$ solution of:
10 drops of $Fe^{2+}$ solution

10 drops of $Fe^{3+}$ solution

For the iron solution that changed the color of permanganate ion, how many drops of $KMnO_4$ was the iron solution able to discolor?

_____

**Part 4** Describe the changes that occurred for the reaction of:
Sodium iodide, NaI, with $Cl_2(aq)$:

Sodium iodide, NaI, with $Br_2(aq)$:

Sodium bromide, NaBr, with $Cl_2(aq)$:

Sodium bromide, NaBr, with $I_2(aq)$:

**Part 5** Describe the changes that occurred for the reaction of:
a.  i.  $MnO_4^-$ with hydrogen peroxide and acid:

ii.  $MnO_4^-$ with hydrogen peroxide without acid:

iii.  $MnO_4^-$ with oxalic acid:

b.  i.  Vanadate ion, $VO_2^+$, and sulfite, $SO_3^{2-}$:

ii.  Vanadyl ion, $VO^{2+}$, and hypochlorite, $OCl^-$:

# Report for Experiment 78

**Name**_____

## Analysis and Conclusions

The list below shows six equations which you will need in order to answer the questions for Parts 1-3. They are called half-reactions because each shows only half of an oxidation-reduction process. They are written twice: first as reductions, then reversed to become oxidations.

$$Zn^{2+} + 2e^- \rightarrow Zn \qquad\qquad Zn \rightarrow Zn^{2+} + 2e^-$$

$$Cu^{2+} + 2e^- \rightarrow Cu \qquad\qquad Cu \rightarrow Cu^{2+} + 2e^-$$

$$Mg^{2+} + 2e^- \rightarrow Mg \qquad\qquad Mg \rightarrow Mg^{2+} + 2e^-$$

$$Fe^{3+} + 1e^- \rightarrow Fe^{2+} \qquad\qquad Fe^{2+} \rightarrow Fe^{3+} + 1e^-$$

$$2H^+ + 2e^- \rightarrow H_2 \qquad\qquad H_2 \rightarrow 2H^+ + 2e^-$$

$$Cl_2 + 2e^- \rightarrow 2\,Cl^- \qquad\qquad 2\,Cl^- \rightarrow Cl_2 + 2e^-$$

### Part 1

1. The only possible states for magnesium are the neutral element (zero charge) and the positive ion, $Mg^{2+}$.

   **a.** What was the initial oxidation state for magnesium?_____

   **b.** What was the oxidation state of magnesium after it reacted with HCl?  _____

   **c.** Was magnesium oxidized or reduced? Explain.

   **d.** Write the half-reaction showing the change for magnesium.

2. The hydrochloric acid solution contains $H^+$ ions and $Cl^-$ ions. Consult the list of half-reactions to decide what gas was formed in the reaction. (**Hint:** Recall that you need one oxidation and one reduction taking place in order to have a complete reaction, so this gas must form as a result of the choice you did *not* select in **1c**, above.) Write the equation for the half-reaction resulting in the evolution of the gas you select.

3. Combine your half-reactions from questions **1** and **2** to write the equation for the complete reaction.

# Report for Experiment 78    Name_____

## Part 2

**4.** Consider the two wells used for zinc and copper.

    **a.** What evidence of reaction did you see, if any?

    **b.** One of the following equations represents the reaction that occurred. Select the correct one and justify your choice.

$$Cu + Zn^{2+} \rightarrow Cu^{2+} + Zn \qquad \text{or} \qquad Cu^{2+} + Zn \rightarrow Cu + Zn^{2+}$$

    **c.** For the reaction equation you selected in **4b**, identify each of the following:

    **i.** The species reduced: _____

    **ii.** The species oxidized: _____

    **iii.** The reducing agent: _____

    **iv.** The oxidizing agent: _____

## Part 3

**5. a.** In which cell did the color of permanganate ion disappear? That is, which test reagent, $Fe^{2+}$ or $Fe^{3+}$, caused the purple color to fade?

    **b.** The permanganate and iron solutions were both 0.1 $M$ yet ten drops of iron solution were able to discolor only a few drops of permanganate solution. What can you conclude about the stoichiometry of the reaction?

**6.** The color change was the result of one of the iron ions being converted to the other oxidation state.

    **a.** Which of the two equations below best illustrates what happened in the well for which you observed the color change? Explain how you arrived at your choice.

$$Fe^{2+} \rightarrow Fe^{3+} + e^{-} \qquad \text{or} \qquad Fe^{3+} + e^{-} \rightarrow Fe^{2+}$$

    **b.** Is iron being oxidized or reduced? Explain.

    **c.** Is permanganate ion being oxidized or reduced? Explain.

# Report for Experiment 78    Name_____

**d.** In the reaction between permanganate and iron ions, which is the oxidizing agent and which is the reducing agent? Explain.

## Part 4

7. The color you saw in step 6 is due to formation of molecular iodine, $I_2$, from iodide ion, $I^-$.
   **a.** Is iodine being oxidized or reduced in this reaction? _____

   **b.** Oxidation and reduction must always occur together. What species in each of the tubes must be causing the change from iodide to iodine?_____

8. In step 7, only one of the halogen solutions was able to change bromide ion, $Br^-$, to molecular bromine, $Br_2$. Which halogen caused the change? _____

9. Look at your combined results from steps 6 and 7, and consider the relative positions of chlorine, bromine and iodine on the periodic table. Make a general statement concerning the relative ease of oxidizing halogen ions to molecular halogens.

## Part 5

10. For the reaction between hydrogen peroxide and potassium permanganate
    **a.** What difference does the presence of sulfuric acid make?

    **b.** What is the gas formed in the reaction?

11. How does the speed of reaction between permanganate and oxalic acid compare with the speed of most of the other reactions in this experiment? What was the effect of warming the system on the speed of reaction?

12. Did the products of the reaction between potassium permanganate and oxalic acid more closely resemble those of the reaction between hydrogen peroxide with sulfuric acid or without? Account for this result.

# Report for Experiment 78

Name_____

13. In the reaction between $KMnO_4$ and $H_2C_2O_4$, a gas was produced as the oxalic acid reacted. What was this gas? (**Hint:** Look at the relative proportions of the elements in oxalic acid.)

14. The sulfite ion changes vanadium from the +5 state to the +4 state.
    a. Is this an oxidation or a reduction? _____
    
    b. What must have happened to the sulfite ion in the process?

15. What effect (oxidation or reduction) does the hypochlorite ion in NaOCl(aq) have on vanadium(IV)? What happens to the vanadium(IV)? How can you tell?

# Report for Experiment 79

## Activity Series

### Data/Observations

**Part 1**

Record your observations in the following table.

|     | $CuCl_2$ | $Fe(NO_3)_2$ | $Zn(NO_3)_2$ | $Mg(NO_3)_2$ | $Al(NO_3)_3$ |
|-----|----------|--------------|--------------|--------------|--------------|
| Cu  |          |              |              |              |              |
| Fe  |          |              |              |              |              |
| Zn  |          |              |              |              |              |
| Mg  |          |              |              |              |              |
| Al  |          |              |              |              |              |

**Part 2:**

Record your observations in the table below.

|     | Cu | Fe | Zn | Mg | Al |
|-----|----|----|----|----|----|
| HCl |    |    |    |    |    |

# Report for Experiment 79

Name_____

## Analysis and Conclusions

**Part I:**

1. Suppose metal "A" reacts with a solution containing ions of metal "B". Can we predict whether or not metal "B" will react with a solution containing ions of metal "A"?

2. According to your results, order the metals from most active to least active. Explain your reasoning. This order is called the activity series.

**Part 2:**

3. Are your results in Part 2 consistent with the activity series you developed in Part 1? Explain. Where would $H^+$ fit in this series?

4. Identify the oxidizing agent and reducing agent in each reaction.

| | oxidizing agent | reducing agent |
|---|---|---|
| **Cu + HCl** | | |
| **Al + HCl** | | |
| **Zn + HCl** | | |
| **Fe + HCl** | | |
| **Mg + HCl** | | |

# Report for Experiment 79

Name_____

5. Do metals react with solutions containing ions of the same metals? Explain the results when a metal was added to a solution containing the same metal.

## Something Extra

Would changing the concentrations of the solutions affect your activity series? Try it.

Name_____

Section_____ Date_____

# Report for Experiment 80

## Halogen Activity Series

### Prelaboratory Questions

1. Write equations for the formation of the halide ions from molecular halogens. Assume the reactions take place in aqueous solution.

2. Do the equations you wrote represent oxidations or reductions? Defend your choice.

3. **a.** Write the equation for the single replacement reaction between aqueous sodium chloride and molecular fluorine.

   **b.** Which species is oxidized? Which is reduced? (Answer using names and symbols of the species involved.)

4. Explain why halide ions dissolve well in water, while molecular halogens do not.

5. Steps 2, 3, and 4 of the procedure each exclude one of the halide ion solutions. Why? **(Hint:** Would chlorine atoms be likely to react with chloride ions by taking away the extra electron?)

# Report for Experiment 80

Name_____

## Data/Observations

**Part 1 Preliminary Tests:**     paint thinner + $Cl_2$ (*aq*):

paint thinner + $Br_2$ (*aq*):

paint thinner + $I_2$ (*aq*):

**Part 2          Activity Tests:**

$Cl_2$ (*aq*)        + paint thinner

+ NaF(*aq*)

+ NaBr(*aq*)

+ NaI(*aq*)

$Br_2$ (*aq*)         + paint thinner

+ NaF(*aq*)

+ NaCl(*aq*)

+ NaI(*aq*)

$I_2$ (*aq*)        + paint thinner

+ NaF(*aq*)

+ NaCl(*aq*)

+ NaBr(*aq*)

## Analysis and Conclusions

1. Write equations for the reactions that took place. You need not write equations for any cases in which there was no evidence of chemical reaction.

# Report for Experiment 80

**Name**_____

2. Examination of your data should let you place bromine, chlorine, and iodine in order of activity. A more active molecular halogen is able to oxidize (take electrons) from less-active halide ions. Once you have established the order for these three, you should be able to place fluorine relative to the others, based on their positions on the periodic table.

3. Suppose you had been provided with a solution of molecular fluorine, $F_2(aq)$. Predict the reactions that you would expect as $F_2(aq)$ is mixed with paint thinner and solutions of the other halides.

4. It would be impossible for your instructor to prepare an aqueous solution of molecular fluorine. Suggest an explanation for this fact.

# Report for Experiment 81

## Analysis of Hydrogen Peroxide

### Prelaboratory Questions

**1.** If antiseptic hydrogen peroxide is 3% $H_2O_2$ by mass, approximately how many moles of $H_2O_2$ are present in each gram of antiseptic solution? You can assume the solution has the same density as water. Show your calculations.

**2.** A solution of potassium permanganate is prepared by dissolving 1.45 g of solid $KMnO_4$ in about 100 mL of water. The total mass of solution is 102.50 g. Assuming the density of the solution is 1.0 g/mL, calculate the concentration of the solution:

**a.** in moles of solute per gram of solution. Show your work.

**b.** in moles of solute per liter of solution (the molarity). Show your work.

**3.** Your three titrations will require a total of about 0.30 mL of 6 $M$ $H_2SO_4$. What mass of sodium bicarbonate would be needed to neutralize this much acid? The molecular equation for the neutralization reaction is:

$$2\,NaHCO_3(s) + H_2SO_4\,(aq) \rightarrow 2\,H_2O(l) + 2\,CO_2(g) + Na_2SO_4(aq)$$

# Report for Experiment 81

**Name**_____

## Data/Observations

### Titration Data

For each of your three titration samples, record the pipet masses, and determine the mass of solution used. Enter the values in the appropriate blanks in the table that follows.

Concentration of $KMnO_4$            _____ mol $KMnO_4$/g solution

#### sample #1

initial mass of $H_2O_2$ pipet and contents      _____ g

final mass of $H_2O_2$ pipet and contents      _____ g

mass of $H_2O_2$ solution used      _____ g

initial mass of $KMnO_4$ pipet and contents      _____ g

final mass of $KMnO_4$ pipet and contents      _____ g

mass of $KMnO_4$ solution used      _____ g

#### sample #2

initial mass of $H_2O_2$ pipet and contents      _____ g

final mass of $H_2O_2$ pipet and contents      _____ g

mass of $H_2O_2$ solution used      _____ g

initial mass of $KMnO_4$ pipet and contents      _____ g

final mass of $KMnO_4$ pipet and contents      _____ g

mass of $KMnO_4$ solution used      _____ g

#### sample #3

initial mass of $H_2O_2$ pipet and contents      _____ g

final mass of $H_2O_2$ pipet and contents      _____ g

mass of $H_2O_2$ solution used      _____ g

initial mass of $KMnO_4$ pipet and contents      _____ g

final mass of $KMnO_4$ pipet and contents      _____ g

mass of $KMnO_4$ solution used      _____ g

# Report for Experiment 81

Name_____

## Analysis and Conclusions

1. Use your data and the concentration provided for the permanganate solution to calculate the number of moles of $KMnO_4$ used in each of your titrations. Show your work for the first titration. Enter values for all three titrations in the Summary Table.

2. Use your results for **1** and the balanced equation given for the reaction between potassium permanganate and hydrogen peroxide to determine the mass and number of moles of hydrogen peroxide that were present in each sample. Show your calculations for the first sample; enter the values for all three in the Summary Table.

3. Use the mass of $H_2O_2$ (from **2**) and the mass of $H_2O_2$ solution used to determine the mass percent of $H_2O_2$ in each sample. Show your work for the first trial; enter all three trials in the Summary Table.

## Summary Table

|  | sample #1 | sample #2 | sample #3 |
|---|---|---|---|
| moles of $KMnO_4$ used | _____ | _____ | _____ |
| moles of $H_2O_2$ in sample | _____ | _____ | _____ |
| mass of $H_2O_2$ in sample | _____ | _____ | _____ |
| percent by mass of $H_2O_2$ | _____ | _____ | _____ |

4. Calculate the average deviation for your three trials. Report the average mass percent of $H_2O_2$ with average deviation here.

_____ ± _____

Average Mass Percent        Average Deviation

# Report for Experiment 81    Name_____

**5.** Discuss the sources of experimental error for this experiment. Remember that errors in calculation and incorrect procedure are not experimental errors.

**6.** Consider the original question: "Does a commercial antiseptic have the full potency claimed on the label?" You've completed your analysis: does it have the strength it is supposed to have? (**Hint:** Notice the number of significant figures claimed by the manufacturer.)

## Something Extra

**1.** Find a bottle of hydrogen peroxide for which the expiration date has passed. With your teacher's permission, devise and carry out experiments to determine how much potency it has lost.

**2.** Exposure to sunlight and heat both tend to hasten the decomposition of hydrogen peroxide. With your teacher's permission design and run experiments to measure the effects of these variables.

# Report for Experiment 82

## Galvanic Cells

## Prelaboratory Questions

**1.** In part 1 of the procedure, is the $Cu^{2+}/Cu$ well the cathode or the anode in each case? Explain.

**2.** Given the nature of the reactions that take place in Part 1, what might you expect to find if you were to weigh the copper electrode before the experiment and again after completion? Why?

## Data/Observations

**Part 1:** Fill in the voltages that you observe for each metal relative to copper. Be sure that each is a positive voltage. Rank the four perimeter metals in terms of their relative difference to copper, with 1 assigned the metal with the largest potential difference.

| Cell Combination | Observed Potential (volts) | Rank vs. Copper |
|---|---|---|
| Mg/Cu | | |
| Fe/Cu | | |
| Pb/Cu | | |
| Zn/Cu | | |

**Part 2:** There are six possible combinations that you can make from the four perimeter metals. Before you proceed to Part 2 of the Procedure, answer Analysis and Conclusions questions **1** and **2**. Place your answers in the Predicted Potential column of the Part 2 Data Table, below. Then as you carry out the second part of the procedure, fill in the observed values.

# Report for Experiment 82

Name_____

| Metal Pair | Anode/Cathode | Predicted Potential (V) | Observed Potential (V) | Deviation (V) | Percent Deviation |
|---|---|---|---|---|---|
| | | | | | |
| | | | | | |
| | | | | | |
| | | | | | |
| | | | | | |
| | | | | | |

## Analysis and Conclusions

1. On the Data Table for Part 1 rank the four perimeter metals in terms of their relative difference to copper, with 1 assigned the metal with the largest potential difference.

2. In Part 1 of the experiment, you determined the reduction potentials for four metals, all relative to copper. Now use these potentials and the ranks that you assigned the four metals to predict the potentials you will get when you connect these metals(in pairs) directly to each other.

   a. By comparing their potentials relative to copper, determine the potential difference between each of the following pairs. Thus, if one metal is 0.75V different than copper, and another is 0.50V different, then the potential difference between the two must be 0.75 - 0.50 = 0.25V. Enter these predicted potential differences in the Data Table for Part 2.

   b. Decide which member of each pair should be the anode (oxidized) and which should be the cathode (reduced). Enter your answers in the Data Table for Part 2.

3. Based on your results, which lead of the voltage probe (red or black) should be connected to the anode and which to the cathode?

4. Determine the difference between each of your predictions and the values you measured in Part 2. Then divide each deviation by the measured value and convert the resulting fraction to a percent. Show one sample calculation and enter that and all other results in the Data Table for Part 2.

5. Determine your experimental values for the standard reduction potentials of each of the other four metals by adding −0.34 V to the observed potentials relative to copper.

| Metal | Reduction Potential | % Error |
|---|---|---|
| Fe | | |
| Pb | | |
| Mg | | |
| Zn | | |

6. Consult an advanced text or a standard reference, such as the CRC *Handbook of Chemistry and Physics* to find the accepted values for iron, lead, magnesium and zinc. Calculate your percent error for each of the values and enter it in the table above. In each case, the percent error is found by dividing the difference between your value and the accepted value, by the accepted value and then convert to percent.

Name_____

Section_____ Date_____

# Report for Experiment 83

## Corrosion of Iron

### Prelaboratory Questions

1. Determine the oxidation number of the iron atom in each of the following compounds:
   a. FeO
   b. $Fe_2O_3$

2. Why must oxidation and reduction always occur simultaneously? In other words, why will there never be an oxidation reaction without an accompanying reduction?

3. What environmental conditions might accelerate the rate at which a metal corrodes? Why?

4. Metals are known to have relatively low ionization energies. How does this fact relate to the ease with which metals corrode?

# Report for Experiment 83

Name_____

## Data/Observations

### Part 1    Reactions of Iron with Aqueous Reagent Solutions

| Test Tube | Reagent | Acid/Base/Neutral | Observations of Reaction |
|-----------|---------|-------------------|--------------------------|
| 1 | | | |
| 2 | | | |
| 3 | | | |
| 4 | | | |
| 5 | | | |

### Part 2    Reactions of Iron with Metals

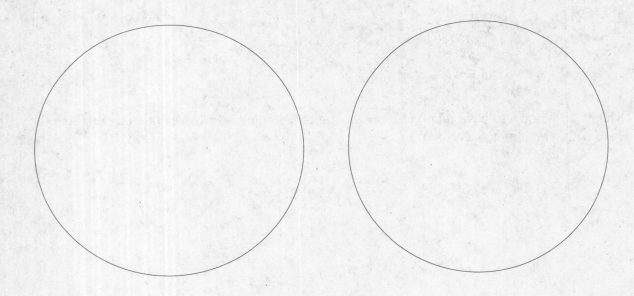

# Report for Experiment 83     Name_____

## Analysis and Conclusions

1. List the reagents in Part 1 for which there was no reaction.  In addition to your own data, report the findings of at least one other lab group which used the same set of reagents you did.

2. List the reagents in Part 1 for which there was indication of corrosion. In addition to your own data, report the findings of at least one other lab group which used the same set of reagents you did.

3. Are there any regularities among the reagents which caused corrosion?  What is evidence that you observe?

4. In Parts 2 and 3, what reactions did you observe at the head of the nail, at the pointed end, and at the sharp bend of the nail?  Were these reactions different from those for the remainder of the nail?  How do you explain this?

5. Iron(II) ions are known to react with the hexacyanoferrate ion of potassium hexacyanoferrate to form a colored precipitate.  Write an equation for this reaction.

# Report for Experiment 83

**6.** In Part 2, what colors appeared in the agar in the Petri dishes? What does each color indicate?

**7.** What color indicates oxidation? What color indicates reduction?

**8.** How does a coating of zinc on iron protect iron from corrosion?

**9.** Why can a nail be stored on the shelf and not rust, but when it is placed in water, it rusts quickly?

## Something Extra

**1.** Consult a reduction potential chart and predict another metal that is more readily oxidized than iron.

**2.** Using chemical resources, investigate the process known as galvanization. How does it relate to your experiment?

# Report for Experiment 84

## Investigating Radioactivity

### Prelaboratory Questions

1. How would the neutron:proton ratio be affected by:
   a. beta radiation? Defend your answer.


   b. positron production? Defend your answer.



2. A proton has a mass of $1.67262 \times 10^{-27}$ kg. The mass of an electron is $9.10939 \times 10^{-31}$ kg.
   a. What is the combined mass of a proton and an electron? Watch your precision!


   b. If a neutron has a mass of $1.67493 \times 10^{-27}$ kg, how much mass is "lost" during beta decay?


   c. If that mass is lost as a photon of electromagnetic radiation, use the equation, $E = mc^2$, to calculate the amount of energy produced in the process.




### Data/Observations

Radioisotope used: _____     Type of emission: _____

Background radiation:_____ cpm (counts per minute)

### Analysis and Conclusions

1. Using either the TRACE function, or STAT/EDIT from your calculator, complete the table below (cpm = counts per minute).

| Distance | 5.0 cm | 10.0 cm | 15.0 cm | 20.0 cm | 25.0 cm |
|---|---|---|---|---|---|
| Intensity (cpm) | _____ | _____ | _____ | _____ | _____ |

# Report for Experiment 84      Name_____

2. Use a piece of graph paper to plot your data of cpm vs. distance. If available, use a French curve to make the best smooth curve. Otherwise do the best you can, freehand, using the screen of your calculator as a guide. Be sure to label the axes and to use scales that fill as much of the graph paper as possible.

3. Describe the shape of your plot. Does increasing the distance by consistent amounts cause the radiation intensity to diminish steadily?

4. Use your graph to estimate the distance at which the radiation from the source is not distinguishable from the background radiation that you measured in **Part 1**.

5. **a.** Calculate the ratio of the intensities for the following pairs of distances.

   10 cm/5 cm = _____       15 cm/10 cm =_____       20 cm/15 cm = _____

   **b.** What can you deduce from the way in which the ratios change?

6. Compare your graph with those produced by teams that used other types of radiation. Are the shapes the same? If so, is the rate of decrease comparable for all three forms of radiation?

7. Radiation, like light or sound, spreads out as it leaves its source. Think about what you see when you drop a pebble in a still pool of water. The sketch below illustrates this spreading effect.

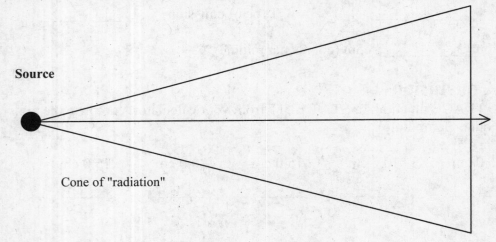

Source

Cone of "radiation"

# Report for Experiment 84

**Name_____**

Mark the center line into segments, such that 2 cm on the scale represents a 5-cm distance from the source. For this purpose, we will assume that the sensor on the radiation monitor can be represented by an object 2 mm across. Place a 2-mm hash-mark at each 2-cm interval, and calculate the fraction of the cone's width that 2-mm represents at that distance. Describe what you find. How does the fraction of the radiation that actually hits the target change as distance increases? This change in intensity is called *attenuation*.

8. The simulation in **7** uses a flat cone to represent the manner in which radiation spreads out. In fact, it spreads out in a full 360° fashion, unless restricted by shielding. How would this change the rate of attenuation?

## Something Extra

1. If your radioactive source has a reasonably short half-life (a few minutes, up to about an hour), use the HALF-LIFE option of the monitor and compare your result with the accepted value for the half-life of the isotope you're testing.

2. With your teacher's approval, design and carry out experiments to investigate various types of shielding, first with paper, then with aluminum foil and lead foil. **Note: lead metal is toxic; use gloves when handling the lead foil. Wash your hands thoroughly after the experiment.]** Consider the following questions:
   • How does the intensity of radiation vary with the type of shielding used?
   • Which type of shielding is the most effective on all three types of radiation?
   • Does shielding affect all types of radiation in the same way, or is one type of radiation easier to stop than others?

# Report for Experiment 85

## The Half-Life of Pennies

### Prelaboratory Questions

1. In this experiment, what do the pennies that land "heads" represent?

2. In this experiment, what do the pennies that land "tails" represent?

3. In this experiment, what does each flip represent?

### Data/Observations

1. Fill in the following table.

| Trial Number | number of pennies flipped |
|:---:|:---:|
| 0 | 100 |
| 1 | |
| 2 | |
| 3 | |
| 4 | |
| 5 | |
| 6 | |
| 7 | |
| 8 | |
| 9 | |
| 10 | |

**2.** How many times did you flip the pennies until no pennies were left?

## Analysis and Conclusions

**1.** Make a graph of number of pennies flipped vs. trial number from your data.

**2.** Gather together all of the class data and make a second graph of the total number of pennies flipped vs. trial number.

**3.** Why is there a difference between the graph of your data and graph of the class data?

**4.** Draw a graph that shows the decay of a 100.0-g sample of a radioactive nuclide with a half-life of 10 years. This should be a graph of mass versus time for the first four half-lives.

# Report for Experiment 85

Name_____

5. Compare the two graphs using your data and the class data to the graph of the 100.0 g sample. Does your graph or the graph of the class data look more like the graph of the 100.0-g sample? Why?

6. Approximately how many half-lives would it take for one mole of a radioactive nuclide to completely disappear?

## Something Extra

Would the shape of the graph change if you used a different number of pennies? Try this activity again with a different number of pennies and comment on the results. Use a wide range (from 10 pennies to a few hundred pennies).

Name_____

Section_____ Date_____

# Report for Experiment 86

# Synthesis of Esters

## Prelaboratory Questions

1. Explain how the reflux condenser helps to keep the liquid reagents from boiling away during the esterification reaction.

2. Using the equation for the reaction between methanol and acetic acid as a model, write the equation for the reaction between methanol and salicylic acid. Consult Chapter 20 of your text for the structure of salicylic acid.

3. Suggest an explanation for the fact that esterification reactions are often referred to as *condensation reactions*.

## Data/Observations

| Reactant | Initial Appearance | Odor (if any) |
|---|---|---|
| Salicylic acid | | |
| Methanol | | |

# Report for Experiment 86

Name_____

Describe what you saw during the refluxing. Could you tell that liquid was being recondensed? If so, what did you see that indicated this was happening?

| Product | Appearance | Odor (if any) |
|---|---|---|
| Methyl salicylate | | |
| Water | | |

## Analysis and Conclusions

1. In this experiment you were interested only in the nature of the products. Explain how you would revise the experiment if the goal was to determine the percent yield. Explain completely what you would do and what measurements would be needed.

320

# Report for Experiment 86

Name_____

## Something Extra

Any number of familiar fragrances can be made from simple, common alcohols and acids, but many of the more familiar ones involve acids or alcohols that have offensive or even toxic properties. Notable are those involving butyric acid, an extremely unpleasant smelling carboxylic acid, resulting in fragrances such as apple and pineapple.

With your teacher's permission try some of the combinations of carboxylic acids and alcohols listed below. Do not create your own combinations without consulting your teacher. The fragrances of some common esters are listed. However, even those for which no fragrance is given will be recognizable.

The procedure for these combinations is the same as before: about 0.5 cm depth of acid, an equal volume of alcohol, and 2-3 drops of sulfuric acid catalyst are refluxed gently for several minutes. Disposal is to be carried out as described under **Cleaning Up**.

| Carboxylic Acid | Alcohol | Fragrance |
| --- | --- | --- |
| acetic acid | ethyl alcohol (ethanol) | _____ |
| acetic acid | amyl alcohol (pentyl alcohol) | banana |
| acetic acid | octyl alcohol | orange |
| acetic acid | *n*-propanol | pear |
| benzoic acid | ethyl alcohol | _____ |
| formic acid | isobutanol | raspberry |
| propionic acid | isobutanol | rum |

Name_____

Section_____ Date_____

# Report for Experiment 87

## Saponification

### Prelaboratory Questions

1. You will prepare a sodium hydroxide solution in this experiment. If 8.0 grams of NaOH are dissolved in enough water to make 25.0 mL of solution, what is the molarity of this solution?

2. Why are many organic molecules nonpolar and, therefore, not water soluble? What property of a soap molecule gives it an affinity for water?

### Data/Observations

1. Describe the appearance of your cooled soap.

# Report for Experiment 87     Name_____

2. Complete the following table by recording your observations from Part 2 of the Procedure.

|  | Experimental Soap | Commercial Detergent | Commercial Soap |
|---|---|---|---|
| **Foaming action** |  |  |  |
| **Reaction with oil and water** |  |  |  |
| **Reaction with CaCl₂** |  |  |  |
| **Reaction with phenolphthalein** |  |  |  |

## Analysis and Conclusions

1. How do the sudsing actions of the soaps and detergent compare?

2. How do the oil breakup capabilities of the soaps and detergent compare?

3. Calcium chloride releases calcium ions into the water. This makes the water "hard". How do the results of the soaps and detergent compare in hard water?

**4.** How do the pH values of the commercial soap and detergent compare with your soap?

## Something Extra

**1.** Check the labels of commercial soaps and detergents. Determine how they are different. What makes a detergent a better choice for use in hard water?

**2.** Making homemade soap can also be done using lard and ashes from a fire. The ashes of burned wood contain sodium and potassium oxides. What happens when these oxides react with water?

Name_____

Section_____ Date_____

# Report for Experiment 88

## Synthesis of Slime

### Prelaboratory Questions

1. Hydrogen bonds are broken as the temperature of the system rises. What would be the expected effect of heating slime?

2. What makes a large molecule such as polyvinyl alcohol soluble in water?

3. Write a balanced molecular equation for the formation of sodium borate and water from boric acid and sodium hydroxide. Formulas are given in Materials.

### Data/Observations

For each step in the procedure, briefly describe **what you did and what you saw**.

**Part 1**

**Step**

1. pH of 0.2 *M* boric acid_____

   pH of 0.2 *M* boric acid + 1 mL 0.2 *M* NaOH  _____

   pH of 0.2 *M* boric acid + 2 mL 0.2 *M* NaOH  _____

   pH of 0.2 *M* boric acid + 3 mL 0.2 *M* NaOH  _____

   Effect of adding NaOH on consistency, etc., of boric acid

2-5.        What you did:                                    What you observed:

# Report for Experiment 88

Name_____

6.        What you did:        What you observed

7.        What you did:        What you observed

**Part 2**
**Step**        What you did:        What you observed

1.

2.

3.

4.

5.

6.

7.

# Report for Experiment 88

**Name_____**

## Analysis and Conclusions

1.  Summarize your observations.  Use complete sentences with correct spelling and grammar.

2.  Describe the effect of sodium borate on the polyvinyl alcohol solution and summarize the properties you discovered for slime.

3.  What difference(s) in the properties of slime did you notice between the product of step 5 and those of the product from step 6?

# Report for Experiment 88

**Name**_____

## Something Extra

The polymers you have investigated used sodium borate to cross-link the long polyvinyl alcohol chains together. But borate ion is not the only substance that can do this cross-linking. Another polymer can be made using sodium silicate in place of sodium borate. Sodium silicate has the empirical formula, $Na_2SiO_3$, but it is, in fact a polymeric chain.

Notice that there is a 1:3 ratio between silicon and oxygen. How might the properties of this polymer differ from those you have observed so far? With your teacher's permission, carry out the following procedure to find out.

1. In a paper cup, mix 2 mL of sodium silicate solution and 10 mL of 4% polyvinyl alcohol solution. Stir the mixture for about a minute and collect the product on the end of the wood stick. Rinse the product briefly with water in a beaker, then squeeze out excess water between paper towels. Compare the properties of this material with the slime you made in the experiment.

2. Try mixing equal volumes of sodium silicate solution with the polyvinyl alcohol solution. Label your cups so that you can note any change in the properties of this material a day or so after it has been prepared.

# Report for Experiment 89

## Gluep

### Data/Observations

1. Write a paragraph discussing your observations when making gluep.

2. How high could your gluep ball bounce?

3. Can gluep lift an image from the newspaper?

4. What happened when vinegar was added to gluep? What happened when baking soda was added?

### Analysis and Conclusions

1. Write a paragraph summarizing the properties of gluep.

# Report for Experiment 89

Name_____

**2.** Explain your observations when gluep reacted with vinegar and baking soda.

## Something Extra

Vary the proportions of water and borax solution in making gluep and retest its properties.

Name_____

Section_____ Date_____

# Report for Experiment 90

## Enzymes in Food

## Prelaboratory Questions

1.  Why is there one sample of gelatin to which nothing was added?

## Data/Observations

List observations for each cup.

| | |
|---|---|
| **Cup 1** | |
| **Cup 2** | |
| **Cup 3** | |
| **Cup 4** | |
| **Cup 5** | |
| **Cup 6** | |
| **Cup 7** | |

## Analysis and Conclusions

1.  Why do many packages of gelatins state "do not use fresh or frozen pineapple"?  Why do the packages not include the statement "do not used canned pineapple?"

# Report for Experiment 90

Name_____

**2.** Is canned pineapple more like fresh, frozen, or microwaved pineapple? What does this tell you about the canning process? Explain.

**3.** From your results, would you say meat tenderizers contain proteases?

**4.** From your results, would you say contact lens cleaners contain proteases?

**5.** Propose a theory of meat tenderizes and contact lens cleaners work.

## Something Extra
How do proteases affect the setting of gelatin? Carry out an experiment to answer this question.

# Report for Experiment 91

## Vitamin C In Juices

## Prelaboratory Questions

1. What is the purpose of the standard vitamin C solution?

2. The vitamin C standard must be freshly prepared and must be kept chilled in order to maintain the proper concentration of vitamin C.
   a. What does this tell you about the effect on vitamin C content of leaving beverage containers open for long periods of time?

   b. How could you experimentally test your hypothesis?

3. In two separate lists, identify the juices that you will test and those that your partner will test.

## Data/Observations

**Concentration of vitamin C standard**

(from stock bottle label): _____ mg/mL

**Drops of iodine needed to titrate 25 drops of:**

Vitamin C standard _____ drops

Identify the juice being tested in the parentheses

beverage #1 (            ) _____ drops

beverage #2 (            ) _____ drops

beverage #3 (            ) _____ drops

beverage #4 (            ) _____ drops

beverage #5 (            ) _____ drops

# Report for Experiment 91

Name_____

## Analysis and Conclusions

In general, fruit juices and fruit drinks are less concentrated, so will require fewer drops of iodine than the standard did, although that is not always the case. By comparing the number of drops of iodine needed for a given beverage with the number needed for the same amount (25 drops) of the Standard, you can get a relative strength comparison. If you then use the actual concentration of the Vitamin C Test solution, you can determine the actual vitamin C concentration in each juice in units of milligrams of Vitamin C per milliliter (mg/mL). Finally, by multiplying this concentration by the number of milliliters in a typical serving, and then comparing your answer with the MRDA for vitamin C, you can decide how much of that particular drink you would need to satisfy your body's need for Vitamin C.

You will do all the calculations for the standard and the five juices that you tested. Your partner will do the same. Later, you will combine your results with those of your partner to see what conclusions you can draw.

1. Calculate the relative concentration of vitamin C in each juice: divide the number of drops of iodine needed for 25 drops of juice by the number of drops needed for 25 drops of Standard. Express the ratio as a decimal with two significant figures. Show your calculations and enter your results in column (b) of the Summary Table.

2. Enter the concentration of the vitamin C standard in column (c) of the Summary Table. This value is the same for all trials. The concentration is found on the stock bottle of vitamin C standard.

3. Find the concentration of vitamin C in each juice by multiplying the ratios you calculated in question 1, above, by the concentration of vitamin C in the standard. Enter the results in column (d) of the table.

4. We will assume that a standard serving of beverage is six fluid ounces (6 fl. oz.), or about 180 mL. Multiply the concentration of each beverage, in mg/mL, by this volume to determine the number of milligrams of vitamin C in one serving. Show your calculations and enter the results in column (e) of your table.

# Report for Experiment 91

Name_____

## Summary Table

| Juice | (a)<br>Drops of<br>Iodine | (b)<br>Conc. of<br>Ratio to<br>Standard | (c)<br>Conc. of<br>Standard<br>(mg/mL) | (d)<br>mg Vitamin C<br>in Juice<br>(mg/mL) | (e)<br>mg Vitamin C<br>in 180 mL<br>of juice |
|-------|-----------|-----------|-----------|-----------|-----------|
| 1 | _____ | _____ | _____ | _____ | _____ |
| 2 | _____ | _____ | _____ | _____ | _____ |
| 3 | _____ | _____ | _____ | _____ | _____ |
| 4 | _____ | _____ | _____ | _____ | _____ |
| 5 | _____ | _____ | _____ | _____ | _____ |

5. The average high school student, male or female, needs about 60 mg of vitamin C per day (this is called the **minimum recommended daily allowance** (MRDA). Consulting with your partner, list the ten juices and drinks in descending order of vitamin C content. In case of ties, use alphabetical order. Make your list in two vertical columns, with the first column containing those that deliver at least the MDRA of vitamin C in one 180-mL serving, and with those that do not in the second column.

6. For each of the juices in your second column (the ones that do not deliver adequate vitamin C in one serving), calculate the volume in milliliters that you would have to drink in order to achieve the 60 mg MDRA.

# Report for Experiment 91

Name_____

7. Do any of the juices surprise you, either by how well or how poorly they tested? In particular, were there any that you thought would perform better than they did?

8. Based on the results of this experiment, and on your own personal preferences, what juice would be the best one to get your 60 mg of vitamin C?

9. While some of the beverages had color, we did not test cola drinks, grape juice or grape drink, or prune juice. Suggest a reason why these would not be suitable for this experiment.

## Something Extra

1. Consult the library or some other reference source to find some sources of vitamin C other than fruits and juices. List two or three of the best ones. How could you test the vitamin C content of a fresh fruit or vegetable that was not in the form of a juice?